NEW ELEMENTARY
MATHEMATICS
SYLLABUS D
2
WORKBOOK

Low Wai Cheng
BSc, Dip Ed

EPB PAN PACIFIC

Published by EPB Pan Pacific

An imprint of Panpac Education Private Limited
Times Centre
1 New Industrial Road
Singapore 536196

Panpac Education

Email: panpmktg@panpaceducation.com
Website: http://www.panpaceducation.com

EPB Pan Pacific is a trademark of Times Publishing Limited

ISBN 978-981-271-943-0

First published 1997
Reprinted 1999
Reprinted 2000
Reprinted 2005 (twice)
Reprinted 2007

Printed by Print Dynamics (S) Pte Ltd

PREFACE

New Elementary Mathematics Workbook 2, a supplement to the textbook *New Elementary Mathematics 2*, is specially written to provide students with additional practice. If follows closely the latest Mathematics Syllabus for Lower Secondary Schools issued by the Ministry of Education, Singapore for use from 1992. Students are required to apply mathematical concepts to real-life problems.

Each *Revision Exercise* covers a few topics and attempts have been made to integrate the appropriate concepts of different topics into a single question. *Test Papers* are provided after every two revision exercises to help reinforce concepts learnt. *Mid-Term* and *Final Term Assessment Papers* have also been included to prepare students for the final examination.

CONTENTS

CHAPTER 1 / Indices

1. Simplify the following, giving each answer in positive index form.

   (a) $(3^{14} \times 3^{-3})^2$

   (b) $14^{-3} \times 14^{-3}$

   (c) $\dfrac{12^4}{9^4}$

   (d) $(2^3)^5 \times (3^4 \times 2^2)^3 \times 3^9 \times \left(\dfrac{1}{4}\right)^0$

   (e) $\dfrac{(7^{-2})^{-3}}{(7^2)^0 \times 7^{-10}}$

   (f) $\dfrac{((2^{-1})^{-1})^{-1} \times 6^4}{2^9 \times 3^{10}}$

   (g) $\dfrac{2^6 \times 8^{-3}}{4^{-3} \times 2^7}$

   (h) $\dfrac{6^{-7} \times 2^{-6}}{9^{-7}} \times \left(\dfrac{3}{4}\right)^{-6}$

   (i) $\dfrac{(15^{-4} \times 15^0 \times 15)^2}{(5^{-1})^8 \times 9^{-4}}$

2. Evaluate the following.

   (a) $\left(\dfrac{2}{5}\right)^3$

   (b) 7^{-2}

   (c) $(0.04)^{-1}$

   (d) $\left(1\dfrac{1}{4}\right)^{-3}$

   (e) $\dfrac{1}{\left(\dfrac{3}{2}\right)^{-2}}$

   (f) -5^0

   (g) $-(2)^6$

   (h) $(-8)^2$

   (i) -4^{-3}

   (j) $(-2)^{-6}$

   (k) $[(-3)^{-1}]^3$

   (l) $[(2^0)^{-1}]^{\frac{1}{2}} \times (2^3)^{-1}$

   (m) $2^3 \times 3^{-3}$

   (n) $2^3 + 2^4$

   (o) $\dfrac{(-2^4)^5}{-(2^5)^4}$

   (p) $\left(\dfrac{4^2}{2^3}\right)^{-2}$

   (q) $1^3 + 2^3 + 3^3$

   (r) $10^3 + 10^1 + 10^0 + 10^{-2}$

3. Evaluate the following.

   (a) $\dfrac{8^{-7}}{4^{-3} \times 4^{-4}}$

   (b) $\dfrac{2^5 \times 3^5}{6^2}$

   (c) $\dfrac{12^3}{4^5 \times 3^2}$

   (d) $\dfrac{4^2 \times 2^{-3}}{3^{-3} \times 6^2}$

   (e) $\dfrac{(-3)^3 \times (-3)^{-6}}{(-2)^{-3}}$

   (f) $\dfrac{2^7 \times 5^8 \times 2}{10^7}$

   (g) $\dfrac{2^4 + 3^4}{5^3 - 5^2}$

   (h) $2^{-4} + \left(\dfrac{1}{3}\right)^{-1}$

   (i) $\left(\dfrac{1}{2}\right)^3 + 4^{-1} + \left(\dfrac{2}{3}\right)^{-2}$

   (j) $\dfrac{(10^{11} \times 10^{-3})^2}{5^{17} \times 2^{17}}$

1

(k) $\left(2\frac{1}{4}\right)^2 \times \left(\frac{2}{3}\right)^3 \div \left(\frac{2}{5}\right)^{-1}$

(l) $\left(\frac{15}{8} - \left(\frac{4}{5}\right)^{-1}\right) \times \left(\frac{5}{2}\right)^{-2}$

(m) $\frac{9^{-1}}{5} + \left(\frac{2}{3}\right)^{-2} \times \left(\frac{9}{4}\right)^{-2}$

(n) $\left(\frac{5}{6}\right)^3 \times \left(\frac{25}{36}\right)^{-2} \div \left(\frac{15}{16}\right)^{-1}$

(o) $5^{\frac{1}{2}} \times 5^{\frac{3}{2}} + \left(7^{\frac{1}{2}}\right)^5 \div 7^{\frac{1}{2}}$

4. Express the following as a single index number with the smallest possible base.

(a) 27×81

(b) $\frac{128}{32}$

(c) $\frac{16}{81} \div 625$

(d) $(81^2)^{-4}$

(e) $\frac{4^8}{8^4}$

(f) $\frac{125^4}{49^6}$

(g) $\left(\frac{81}{36}\right)^3$

(h) $\frac{(16^2)^3}{(8^3)^2}$

(i) $4(2^5)^3$

(j) $\frac{2^{n+3} \times 2^{2n}}{8^{n+1}}$

5. Given that $a = 2$, $b = -2$ and $c = -\frac{1}{2}$, calculate the following.

(a) a^b

(b) b^a

(c) bc^a

(d) $(ac)^b$

(e) c^{a+b}

(f) $a^a(b^a - c^a)$

(g) $\frac{a^2 + b^2 + c^2}{a^2 - b^2 - c^2}$

(h) $a^3 + 3a + 3^a$

6. Solve for x and y if

(a) $(10^4)^y = \frac{1}{10^4} = 10^x$,

(b) $(2^y)^3 = 2x^3 = 16$.

7. Simplify the following and express your answers in positive index form.

(a) $\frac{a^7}{a^{-2}} \times \frac{a^3}{a^4} \div \frac{a^5}{a^2}$

(b) $\frac{(a^3 \times a^2)^5}{a^9 \times a^{10}}$

(c) $\frac{5a^7 \times 4(a \times a^3)^4}{(a^{-3} \times a^2)^5}$

(d) $\frac{(a^{-3} \times a^2)^{-4}}{a^2 \times a^3} \div \frac{2a^{-4} \times a^5}{a^2 \times a^{-6}}$

(e) $4a^3 \times 3a^{-4} \div 9a^{-6}$

(f) $\frac{32a^6b^4}{6a^2b \times (4ab)^2}$

(g) $\frac{10(pq)^3}{(2q)^3 p^5} \div \frac{45p}{(6q)^2}$

(h) $(3p^4 \times p^0 \times p^{-5})^3$

(i) $\frac{m}{5} \times \left(\frac{5}{m^2}\right)^2$

(j) $8(x^{-2}y^3)^4 \times (2xy^2)^{-2}$

(k) $\frac{(2ab^{-2})^3}{4a^5b^3}$

(l) $(a^3 \times a^{-2})^5 \div a^{-5} \div a^{-7}$

(m) $(a^{-2})^0 \div a^{-3} \div a^5 \times a^7 + a^5$

(n) $2a^2 \times 3a^2 \times 4a^2$

(o) $2a^2 + 3a^2 + 4a^2$

(p) $(a^3b^2)^3 \div (a^2b^0)^{-2}$

2

(q) $(3s^2)^2 \times \left(\dfrac{s^2}{3t}\right)^{-3}$

(r) $\dfrac{(-3a)^2 \times -a^2}{9a^3}$

(s) $\dfrac{(-2a^3)^3}{(2a^{-2})^{-3}}$

(t) $\dfrac{(x^2y^3)^{-2} \times (-xy)^5}{(-x^5y^7)^3}$

(u) $\dfrac{9x^3y^4z}{15x^7yz^3} \div \dfrac{6xy^7z^4}{(5xyz^3)^2}$

(v) $\dfrac{2a^{-7}b^2}{b^{-4}c^{-2}} \times \dfrac{ab^{-1}}{3} \div \dfrac{(8ab)^{-1}}{c}$

(w) $\dfrac{(2^3x^2y^4)(5x^3y^2)^{-2}}{(10x^{-2}y^{-3})^{-2}}$

(x) $\dfrac{4x^{-1}y}{(x^2y)(2x^{-3}y)^3}$

(y) $\dfrac{9m^2u}{6n^3u^2} \div \dfrac{24m}{15nu^2} \times \dfrac{8n^2}{10m^3u}$

(z) $\dfrac{2a^{n+2}}{b^n} \div \dfrac{4a^n}{5b^{n-3}} \times \dfrac{6ac^3}{15bc^{n+4}}$

8. Simplify the following.

(a) $(-x^4)^3$

(b) $-3(x^2)^4$

(c) $\dfrac{(a^4)^6}{-a^3 \times (-a^2)^9}$

(d) $(2a^{-1})^4$

(e) $\dfrac{(-p^4)^5}{-(p^5)^4}$

(f) $\dfrac{(-x^3)^{-6} \times (y^2)^{-4} \times -z^5}{(x^{-9})^2 \times y^{-8} \times (-z^2)^{-3}}$

(g) $\dfrac{(ab)^{-4}(abc)^5}{(2ab^2)^2(3abc^2)^{-3}}$

(h) $x^{-4} \div x^{-7} \div x^{-2}$

(i) $(a^2 \times a^{-5})^{-3}$

(j) $(pqr)^{-2} \times (p^2q^3)^2 \div (p^4r^3s)^{-7}$

(k) $\dfrac{(8a^5b^4)(3a^2b^5)^3}{(9ab^2)(2ab)^3}$

(l) $\dfrac{(ab^2)^3}{(a^2b)^4} \times \dfrac{(a^3b^2)^2}{(b^3)^3}$

(m) $\dfrac{(p^2q^{-3})^4}{(q^4r^3)^2} \times \dfrac{(q^{-2}r^5)^6}{(p^{-3}r^4)^3}$

(n) $\dfrac{a^2b^{-5}}{c^3} \times \dfrac{(a^{-2}b)^3}{(ac^2)^4} \div \dfrac{ab^{-2}}{(bc^3)^2}$

(o) $\dfrac{(12p^3q^3)^2}{3pq^{10}} \times \dfrac{(3q^2)^2}{24p^5}$

9. Find the value of x in each of the following.

(a) $4^x = \dfrac{1}{64}$

(b) $3^{-x} = 81$

(c) $8^{-x} = \dfrac{1}{2}$

(d) $125^x = \dfrac{1}{5}$

(e) $2^x \div 2^3 = 32$

(f) $5^4 \times 125 = 5^x$

(g) $8^x = 128^3$

(h) $9^x \times 3^3 = 27$

(i) $27^x = 9^{x-1}$

(j) $2(9^x) = 54$

(k) $9^{x-2} = 81^{7-x}$

(l) $(3x)^{-2} = 9$

(m) $3x^{-4} = \dfrac{1}{27}$

(n) $49^{3x} \times 7^{2x-5} = 343$

(o) $\left(\dfrac{3}{2}\right)^x \times \left(\dfrac{4}{9}\right)^{-x} = 3\dfrac{3}{8}$

10. Solve the following equations.

(a) $4x^2 = 1.44 \times 10^{-4}$

(b) $\dfrac{4}{5}x^3 = 21\dfrac{3}{5}$

3

(c) $\dfrac{3}{x^2} = 16\dfrac{1}{3}$

(d) $-\dfrac{4}{x^3} = 0.5$

(e) $\sqrt[3]{x} = -\dfrac{1}{2}$

(f) $-7\sqrt{x} = 4$

(g) $32^x = 0.5$

(h) $10^x = 0.1$

(i) $8^x = 0.125$

(j) $(0.1)^x = 100$

(k) $\left(\dfrac{2}{5}\right)^x = 0.16$

(l) $(0.3)^x = 3\dfrac{1}{3}$

(m) $\left(\dfrac{16}{81}\right)^x = 3\dfrac{3}{8}$

(n) $\left(\dfrac{10}{3}\right)^x = 0.09$

(o) $(0.4)^x = 6\dfrac{1}{4}$

(p) $243^{-x} = 27$

(q) $\left(\dfrac{4}{9}\right)^{-x} = \dfrac{3}{2}$

(r) $10^{x-3} = 1$

(s) $10^{2x+1} = 0.001$

(t) $16^{\frac{3x+1}{4}} = 2$

(u) $2^x \times 2^{3x-1} = 2$

(v) $3^{3x-1} \div 9^{x+1} \times 27^{x+2} = 81$

(w) $a^{x-3} \div a^{3-x} = a$

(x) $\left(\dfrac{a}{b}\right)^{2x} \times \left(\dfrac{b}{a}\right)^{1-x} = \left(\dfrac{a}{b}\right)^3$

(y) $4^x \times 3^{2x} = 6$

11. Express the following in ordinary notation.
    (a) 2.48×10^{-3}
    (b) 4.125×10^5
    (c) $5.01 \times 10^7 \times 4 \times 10^{-5}$
    (d) $8 \times 10^3 + 8 \times 10 + 8 + 8 \times 10^{-2}$
    (e) $\dfrac{2.24 \times 10^{-1}}{4 \times 10^2}$
    (f) $4.2 \times 10^{-2} - 3 \times 10^{-3}$

12. Express the following in standard form.
    (a) $23\,400$
    (b) $0.005\,089$
    (c) 0.57×0.3
    (d) 347.17×10^{-5}
    (e) 0.216×10^7
    (f) $\dfrac{1.26 \times 10^{-5}}{7 \times 10^{-2}}$
    (g) $\dfrac{27 \times 10^5 \times 0.03 \times 10^{-2}}{4.5 \times 10^{-3}}$
    (h) $(7 \times 10^{-3})^2 - 3(4 \times 10^{-7})$

13. Express $1.5 \times 15 \times 150$ in scientific notation.

14. Express the following in standard form.
    (a) 12 m in cm
    (b) $0.6\ \text{m}^2$ in km^2
    (c) $\dfrac{1}{8}$ g in kg
    (d) $44\dfrac{1}{5}\,l$ in ml
    (e) $\dfrac{1}{2}\ \text{m}^3$ in cm^3

15. Given that $p = 2.8 \times 10^3$ and $q = 4 \times 10^{-2}$, calculate the following, expressing each answer in standard form.
    (a) pq
    (b) $p + q$

(c) $\dfrac{p}{q}$ **(d)** $p - \dfrac{1}{q}$

16. If $a = 2.4 \times 10^{-4}$ and $b = 4 \times 10^{-2}$, find the value of
    (a) $b - a$, giving your answer in decimal, correct to two significant figures,
    (b) b^3, giving your answer in the form $A \times 10^n$, where $1 \leqslant A < 10$ and n is an integer,
    (c) $\dfrac{5a}{3b}$, giving your answer in ordinary notation.

17. Given that $x = 8 \times 10^{-3}$ and $y = 5 \times 10^{-7}$, find $\dfrac{x^2 - 8y}{xy}$ in the form $A \times 10^n$, where $1 \leqslant A < 10$ and n is an integer.

18. Without using a calculator, but with essential workings, arrange the numbers
    (a) 6.4×10^{-8}, 2.8×10^{-7}, 43×10^{-9} in descending order,
    (b) $2^3 \times 3^7 \times 7^6$, $2^5 \times 3^6 \times 7^5$, $2^4 \times 3^7 \times 7^5$ in ascending order.

19. Given that $a = 6.4 \times 10^7$, find the value of
    (a) $\sqrt{a}$, **(b)** $\sqrt[3]{a}$.

20. With the help of a calculator, express the following in standard form, giving the answers correct to three significant figures.
    (a) $84.3 \times 0.041\,8 \times 10^{-2}$
    (b) $\dfrac{1.7^3 + 2.1^2}{(\sqrt{11})^9}$
    (c) $\dfrac{1.48 \times 10^5 + 34.4 \times 10^4}{3.7 \times 10^{-3} \times 0.061 \times 10^{-4}}$
    (d) $\dfrac{(12.3 \times 10^{-2})^{-4}}{127^{0.5} \times 3^{-7}}$
    (e) $\dfrac{4.1 \times 10^3}{\sqrt{5.75^3 - 17\pi}}$
    (f) $\sqrt[3]{\left(\dfrac{5}{8}\right)^2 \times \left(3\dfrac{1}{4}\right)^2 \div \left(\dfrac{4}{7}\right)^4}$
    (g) $\left(\dfrac{1}{0.041\,3}\right)^{\frac{2}{3}} \div [\pi + (0.31)^{-2}]$
    (h) $\dfrac{0.83^4 \times 5 + 4 \times 2.31^3}{6.1^2 \times \sqrt{5.21} - 3 \times \sqrt[3]{48.84}}$
    (i) $\dfrac{27^{-\frac{1}{4}} + \left(\dfrac{2}{3}\right)^{-6} \times \left(\dfrac{1}{5.7}\right)^3}{4^{\frac{2}{3}} - 3^{\frac{1}{3}}}$
    (j) $\dfrac{3.87 \times 10^3 \times 2.09 \times 10^{-2} \times 3.56}{4 \times 0.365 \times 10^4 \div 2.61 \times 10^{-1}}$
    (k) $\left(5\dfrac{7}{9}\right)^{-3} \times (3.125)^{-2} \div \left(\dfrac{3}{7}\right)^5$

21. Express $3.95 \times 10^5\,\text{m}$
    (a) as a whole number, correct to two significant figures,
    (b) **(i)** as a percentage,
    (ii) in km,
    giving your answers in standard form.

22. Find x in each of the following.
    (a) $2^{10} \times 2^x = 4^5$
    (b) $\left(\dfrac{3}{4}\right)^x = 1\dfrac{7}{9}$

1. Using the special algebraic rules, calculate the following.
   (a) 295×305
   (b) $49^2 + 98 + 1$
   (c) $299^2 - 298^2$
   (d) $72.9^2 + 27.1 \times 72.9$
   (e) $39 \times 23 - 23 \times 29$
   (f) 398^2
   (g) $98 \times 0.46 + 98 \times 0.78 - 49 \times 0.48$
   (h) $1\,985^2 - 1\,990 \times 1\,980$
   (i) $(\sqrt{8} - \sqrt{2})^2$
   (j) $\dfrac{5.4^2 - 5.3^2}{5.3 \times 4 + 4 \times 5.4}$
   (k) $\dfrac{123 \times 16 - 16 \times 113}{232^2 - 168^2}$
   (l) $1\,230\,003^2 - 1\,230\,002^2$
   (m) $55^2 - 550 + 25$

2. (a) Given that $7.85^2 - 4.15^2 = 12k$, find the value of k.
   (b) Given that $x^2 + y^2 = 13$ and $xy = -3$, calculate the values of $(x + y)^2$ and $(x - y)^2$.
   (c) If $u - v = 8$ and $u^2 - v^2 = 28$, find the value of $(u + v)$.
   (d) If $(x - y)^2 = 11$ and $2xy = 3$, calculate the value of $x^2 + y^2$.
   (e) Given that $11x = 8.25 \times 2.75 + 8.25^2$, find the value of x.
   (f) Given that $x + y = 7$ and $(x - y) = -3$, find the value of
   (i) $x^2 - 2xy + y^2$,
   (ii) $2x^2 + 4xy + 2y^2$,
   (iii) $3x^2 - 3y^2$.

3. Express the following as fractions with a single denominator.
   (a) $2\frac{1}{5}a - \frac{3}{4}(a + 1)$
   (b) $\dfrac{x + 3y}{2} - \dfrac{x - 7y}{4} + \dfrac{1}{3}$
   (c) $\dfrac{x + 3}{2} - \dfrac{11 - x}{5} - \dfrac{3x - 1}{20}$
   (d) $\dfrac{x + 2}{3} + \dfrac{3(x - 2)}{4} - \dfrac{2(2x + 1)}{5}$
   (e) $\dfrac{2y}{x} - \dfrac{3}{xy} + \dfrac{4x}{y}$
   (f) $\dfrac{2}{a} - \dfrac{3}{2a^2}$
   (g) $\dfrac{1}{x} + \dfrac{1}{12x} - \dfrac{4}{3x}$
   (h) $\dfrac{a + 3x}{2a} + \dfrac{a - x}{6a} - \dfrac{2x + a}{3a}$
   (i) $\left(\dfrac{5}{3xy}\right)^{-2} \div \dfrac{12xy}{15} + \dfrac{3xy}{4}$
   (j) $\dfrac{b - c}{bc} + \dfrac{c - a}{ac} + \dfrac{a - b}{ab}$
   (k) $\dfrac{a - b}{ab} + \dfrac{b - c}{bc} - \dfrac{c - a}{ac}$
   (l) $\dfrac{5}{x - 2} + \dfrac{4}{x + 2}$
   (m) $\dfrac{x}{x + 1} - \dfrac{y}{y + 1}$
   (n) $\dfrac{4}{x - 2} - \dfrac{7}{4 - 2x} + \dfrac{5}{3(x + 2)}$

(o) $\dfrac{4c}{10c - 5d} + \dfrac{2d}{6c - 3d}$

(p) $\dfrac{6q}{2q + 3r} - 3$

(q) $\dfrac{a + 1}{2a - 8} - \dfrac{a + 2}{12 - 3a}$

(r) $\dfrac{1}{(2a - 3)} - \dfrac{2}{(3 - 2a)} + \dfrac{18}{(3 - 2a)(3 + 2a)}$

(s) $\dfrac{3}{p + 3r} - \dfrac{3p}{(p + 3r)(p - 3r)}$

(t) $\dfrac{m}{2m - 1} + \dfrac{m^2 + 12m - 5}{(2m - 1)(m + 2)} - \dfrac{5}{m + 2}$

(u) $\dfrac{5}{2(e - f)} + \dfrac{4}{3(f - e)}$

(v) $\left(\dfrac{1}{x} - \dfrac{3}{x^2} - \dfrac{4}{x^3}\right) \cdot \left(\dfrac{4x}{x - 4} + \dfrac{x}{x + 1}\right)$

(w) $\left(\dfrac{x}{x - 2} + \dfrac{3}{x + 2}\right) \div \left(\dfrac{4}{x - 2} - \dfrac{3}{x}\right)$

(x) $\dfrac{1}{x + 1} + \dfrac{3}{x - 1} + \dfrac{2x}{1 - x^2}$

(y) $\dfrac{3}{x + 1} + \dfrac{4}{x + 2} - \dfrac{2x + 5}{(x + 1)(x + 2)}$

(z) $\dfrac{7}{x^2 + 3x - 10} - \dfrac{2}{x^2 + 5x} - \dfrac{2}{x^2 - 2x}$

4. Expand and simplify the following.

(a) $3(2x - 5) - 2(2x + 3)$

(b) $-4x^2(x^3 - 8)$

(c) $(3p + 2)(5p - 4)$

(d) $(4 - k)(2 + 7k)$

(e) $6a + [5a - 3(a - 2)]$

(f) $3(2a + 1)(3a - 2)$

(g) $(5m^2 - n)(m + 2n^2)$

(h) $(x^2 - 6x - 1)(2x + 3)$

(i) $(1 + u + u^2)(2 - u + 3u^2)$

(j) $(x - 3)(2x + 4) - 3(x + 5)(x - 1)$

(k) $(x^2 + 3x)(x^2 - 3)$

(l) $a^2(3a - 1)(a^2 - 6)$

(m) $\dfrac{-5}{x^2}(3x^4 - 2x^3 + 6x^2)$

(n) $8x - [(2x - 1) - (4x + 5)]$

(o) $9x - [(2x - 1)(4x + 5)]$

(p) $-8x[(2x - 1) - (4x + 5)]$

(q) $-8x[(2x - 1)(4x + 5)]$

(r) $4m - 3(3m - 2)(m + 1)$

(s) $(2x + 1)(x^2 - 3) - 2(3x^2 - 3x)$

(t) $2\left[y - \dfrac{3}{2}(2y - x)\right] - 3x$

(u) $3(2x + 1) - 4[2x - (x + 5)]$

(v) $2b(c - a) - [3c(a - b) - 3a(b + c)]$

(w) $5[x - 3(x - 2(x + y))] - 3[x - 2(x - 3(x + y))]$

5. Expand and simplify the following.

(a) $(x^3 + x^5)^2$

(b) $(2a^2 - 3b^3)^2$

(c) $(2p^5q + 1)(2p^5q - 1)$

(d) $(x - y)(x + y)(x^2 + y^2)$

(e) $(a + 4)^2 + (a - 4)^2$

(f) $(a + b + c + d)(a + b - c - d) + (c + d)^2$

(g) $(3a + 1)(3a - 1)^2$

(h) $3(2a - 3)^2 - 2(2a - 3)(2a + 3)$

(i) $4a(a + 4) - (a + 1)^2$

(j) $(2x + 5)^2 - 2x + 5(2x - 5)$

(k) $(2y - 3)^2 - (2y + 3)^2$

7

Factorise the following expressions completely.

6. $p^2z^3 + p^3z^4 - p^4z^5$

7. $3x^2 + 9x^3y + 12x^2y^2$

8. $3x^2 + 27$

9. $2x^3 - 32xy^2$

10. $4m^3n^2 - 9mn^3$

11. $x^2 + 3xy - 4y^2$

12. $1 - p - 12p^2$

13. $54a^5 - 6a^3$

14. $3uv + 2v - 12u - 8$

15. $20rc - 4rd - 15qc + 3qd$

16. $(y + 5)^2 - (y - 5)^2$

17. $9(x - 3y)^2 - 144(2x + y)^2$

18. $3a(x - 3) - 6b(x - 3)$

19. $pn^2 + 3np - 28p$

20. $x^2y - 2xy - 3y$

21. $p(4m - n) - 2p(m + 2n)$

22. $2x + 4y - 3(x + 2y)^2$

23. $16x^4 - y^8z^{16}$

24. $8x - 10 + 2x^2$

25. $6x^2 - 1 + 5x$

26. $1 - 5xy + 6x^2y^2$

27. $2 - 5x - 12x^2$

28. $26x - 8x^2 - 6$

29. $36a^2 + 6a^3 + 54a$

30. $8x^2y^4 - 56x^3y^3 + 98x^4y^2$

31. $2a^2p - a^2 + 4 - 8p$

32. $y^3 + y^2 - y - 1$

33. $5a^2 - a(2a - 30)$

34. $(p - 3q)^2 - (p - 3q)(p + 2q)$

35. $(a - 3b)(4x + 5y) - (a - 3b)(5y + z)$

36. $a^2 + a^3 - 4(1 + a)$

37. $243x^7 - 3x^3$

38. $-5y^2 - y + 6$

39. $2a^3b^2c - 8a^5b^4c - 6a^3b^5c^2$

40. $16x^{16} - 1$

41. $4a(2a + 3) - 3a^2 - 2a^3$

42. $4x^2y + 6xy^2 - 4x - 6y$

43. $(3p + q)(5 - 3x^2) - (5 - 4x^2)(3p + q)$

44. $25x^4 - (x^2 - x)^2$

45. $(a + b)^2 - 2(a + b) - 63$

46. $a^2 + 2a^2b - 16(1 + 2b)$

47. $3(a + 2b)^2 - 9a - 18b$

48. $5(5 - x) - 5y(x - 5)$

8

49. Solve the following equations.

(a) $\dfrac{3 - 5x}{4} = \dfrac{1}{8}$

(b) $\dfrac{3y}{4} - \dfrac{y - 1}{2} = -1$

(c) $\dfrac{7x - 4}{15} + \dfrac{x - 1}{3} = \dfrac{1 - 3x}{5} - \dfrac{7 + x}{10}$

(d) $\dfrac{3m}{2} - \dfrac{4(m - 3)}{7} = \dfrac{1}{14} + \dfrac{5(2 - 3m)}{28}$

(e) $1 = \dfrac{7}{3} + \dfrac{5}{e}$

(f) $\dfrac{r}{3} + \dfrac{2r - 1}{2} = 3(r + 4)$

(g) $\dfrac{x}{x + 2} - \dfrac{3}{5} = 0$

(h) $\dfrac{6}{x} + \dfrac{3}{x + 1} = 0$

(i) $\dfrac{3}{x - 5} - 5 = \dfrac{2}{5 - x}$

(j) $\dfrac{4}{2x - 2} + \dfrac{1}{1 - x} = 4$

(k) $\dfrac{10}{2b - 5} - \dfrac{3}{b - 3} = 0$

(l) $\dfrac{2}{d + 3} - \dfrac{d - 6}{(d + 3)(d - 3)} = 0$

(m) $\dfrac{3}{m - 4} - \dfrac{m + 2}{(m - 4)(m + 1)} = \dfrac{1}{2(m + 1)}$

(n) $7 + \dfrac{3}{2(1 - 2x)} = \dfrac{1}{2(2x - 1)} - 1$

(o) $\dfrac{5y}{y + 5} - 2 = \dfrac{1}{4} + \dfrac{5}{2(y + 5)}$

50. Expand and simplify the following.

(a) $(4 - a)(4 + a) - 2(a + 3)^2$

(b) $\dfrac{3}{x - 3} + \dfrac{5x}{6 - 2x}$

(c) $\dfrac{x + 3}{2} - \dfrac{11 - x}{5} = \dfrac{4x + 1}{20}$

51. Evaluate the following by special algebraic rules.

(a) 118^2

(b) 118×122

(c) $\dfrac{56 \times 5.2 + 5.2 \times 34}{7.6^2 - 2.4^2}$

52. Solve the following equations.

(a) $\dfrac{3}{x - 3} - \dfrac{2}{4x + 1} = \dfrac{1}{4x + 1}$

(b) (i) $4 + 2x(x - 3) = 0$

　　 (ii) $(4 + 2x)(x - 3) = 0$

53. How can the number 42 be divided into two parts in order that the sum of $\dfrac{2}{3}$ of one part and $\dfrac{3}{4}$ of the other part is 30?

54. Lisa's age is $\dfrac{2}{3}$ that of Leslie's. Two years ago, Lisa's age was $\dfrac{1}{2}$ of what Leslie's will be in five years' time. How old are they now?

9

55. One half of what Mary's age was four years ago is equal to one third of what her age will be in five years' time. How old is Mary now?

56. A man cycles for some distance at 16 km/h and another of the same distance at 15 km/h. The total time taken is $7\frac{3}{4}$ hours. Find the total distance travelled.

57. A girl has a certain number of biscuits. If she eats 16 biscuits a day, they will last her six days less than if she eats 12 biscuits a day. How many biscuits does she have?

58. A certain number of straws can be divided evenly among 24 boxes. If each box had 3 more straws instead, 20 boxes could be filled evenly, and the rest would be empty. How many straws are there?

59. Mrs Wu buys 32 kg of flour at a certain price. She finds that if she buys some cheaper flour costing 15 cents less per kg, she can buy $2\frac{1}{2}$ kg more for the same amount of money. What is the price per kg of the cheaper flour?

60. A man travels regularly between two places. He takes $3\frac{1}{4}$ hours if he travels at his usual speed. He finds that if he increases his speed by 4 km/h, he can reduce the time taken by 10 minutes. What is his usual speed?

61. Jimmy cycles from his house to school at a usual speed of 30 km/h. He finds that if he increases his speed by 15 km/h, he can reach his school 15 minutes earlier. Find the distance he cycles. Find also the time required for the journey.

62. A driver took $3\frac{1}{12}$ hours to travel 150 km. He drove part of the distance at a uniform speed of 48 km/h and part of the distance at 72 km/h. What is the distance he travelled at 48 km/h? How much time did he take to travel the distance at 72 km/h?

63. A cyclist travels 60 km. If he reduces his speed by 2 km/h, he will take one hour longer. Find the original speed of the cyclist.

TEST PAPER 1

Time : 1 hour
Marks : 50

*Answer all the questions **without** the use of a calculator.*

1. Express $\frac{3}{70}$
   (a) as a decimal, correct to three decimal places, [1]
   (b) in standard form, correct to three significant figures. [1]

Ans (a) _____

(b) _____

2. Given that $a = 4.8 \times 10^{-5}$ and $b = 9.6 \times 10^{-4}$, find, expressing your answer in standard form, the value of

   (a) $a + b$,   (b) $\frac{30a}{b}$. [4]

Ans (a) _____

(b) _____

3. Evaluate the following.

(a) $5^{-1} \times 1^{-5}$ [2]

Ans _____

(b) $\dfrac{2^4 \times 3^3}{6^4}$ [2]

Ans _____

(c) $(-2)^3 + 2^{-3} \times \left(\dfrac{1}{16}\right)^{-1}$ [3]

Ans _____

(d) $\left(\dfrac{5^{-1}}{4}\right)^{-2} \times (2^3)^{-2}$ [3]

Ans _____

4. Simplify the following, expressing each answer in positive index form.

(a) $\dfrac{5^{-13} \times 10^{13} \times 2^8}{(2^7)^{-2}}$ [4]

Ans _____

(b) $ab^{-1} \times (2ab)^{-2}$ [2]

Ans _____

(c) $\dfrac{(-a)^3 \times -a^4}{a^{-5} \times (-a)^6}$ [3]

Ans _____

13

(d) $\dfrac{6(ab^3)^3}{(-2a^{-2}b^8)^2}$ [3]

Ans _____

5. Expand and simplify the following.
   (a) $(2 - 3m)(1 - 2m + 4m^2)$ [2]

Ans _____

   (b) $2 - [2x - 3(x - 5)]$ [2]

Ans _____

6. Factorise the following completely.
  (a) $4a^4 - 64$ [2]

Ans _____

  (b) $4m^2 + 3n^2 - 8mn$ [2]

Ans _____

  (c) $3a + 6ab - 3(1 + 2b)$ [3]

Ans _____

7. Simplify the following algebraic fractions.

(a) $\dfrac{7a^4b^3}{24b^{10}c^3} \div \dfrac{a^2c}{18b^7c^4} \times \dfrac{4}{21a^2}$ [2]

Ans _____

(b) $\dfrac{1}{n} - \dfrac{1}{n(n+1)}$ [3]

Ans _____

8. Solve the following equations.

(a) $\dfrac{x}{3} = 2\dfrac{1}{3} + \dfrac{3-2x}{5}$ [3]

Ans _____

(b) $\dfrac{1}{2(3x-1)} + \dfrac{1}{4(1-3x)} = 5$ [3]

Ans _____

1. **(a)** Find x in terms of a, b, c and d in this equation: $ax - b = cx + d$.

   (b) Solve $x - 2.13 = 0.75x + 1.17$.

2. **(a)** Find x in terms of a, b, c and d in this equation: $a(b - cx) = b(dx - c)$.

   (b) Solve $\frac{1}{3}\left(4 - \frac{2}{3}x\right) = 4\left(\frac{4}{9}x - \frac{2}{3}\right)$.

3. **(a)** Find x in terms of a, b and c in this equation: $\frac{x}{2a} + \frac{x}{b} = 5c$.

   (b) Solve $\frac{x}{6} + \frac{x}{3} = 10$.

4. Given $a - \{bx - (ax - b) - a\} = bx$, find
   (a) x in terms of a and b,
   (b) b in terms of a and x.

5. Rewrite each of the following formulae as indicated.

   (a) $y = \dfrac{x(2z + 1)}{x + 2k}$, make x the subject.

   (b) $x = \sqrt{\dfrac{y + 1}{z}}$, express y in terms of x and z.

   (c) $s = \dfrac{2k - 3a}{5b - k}$, find k in terms of a, b and s.

   (d) $y + 2 = \dfrac{3y + k}{a}$, make y the subject.

   (e) $\dfrac{3a + b}{2a - b} = \dfrac{2}{5}$, express a in terms of b.

   (f) $3a = \dfrac{2}{b} + \dfrac{1}{c}$, make b the subject.

   (g) $b^2 = \dfrac{3b}{5x - 4y}$, make y the subject.

   (h) $p = \dfrac{m(v^2 - u^2)}{2gx}$, make u the subject.

6. Make x the subject of the formula in each of the following.
   (a) $(x - y)^2 = 2y - 5$ **(b)** $3x - y = xz + 5$

   (c) $y = \dfrac{x + 2a}{a}$ **(d)** $\dfrac{2}{x + p} = \dfrac{3}{q}$

(e) $a - x = \dfrac{3x + 7}{a}$

(f) $\dfrac{1}{2w} = \dfrac{2}{3x} + \dfrac{3}{4u}$

(g) $\dfrac{2x + y}{2x - y} = \dfrac{3}{4}$

(h) $y = \sqrt[3]{3x^2 - a}$

7. Given that $bp = a + \dfrac{bv^2}{k}$, express

   (a) v in terms of p, a, b and k,

   (b) b in terms of p, a, v and k.

8. The formula used in an experiment is given by $E = \dfrac{w}{w + x}$.

   (a) Find the value of E when $w = 30$ and $x = 18$.

   (b) Express w in terms of E and x.

9. (a) Express y in terms of x if $x = \dfrac{x + 3y}{y - x}$.

   (b) Hence find the value of y when $x = -1$.

10. Given that $y = 3(2a - b)$,

    (a) evaluate y if $a = -8$ and $b = -3$,

    (b) express b in terms of a and y.

11. $M = \dfrac{1}{2}x^2y - 2xz$

    (a) Evaluate M when $x = 4.2 \times 10^4$, $y = 2.7 \times 10^{-6}$ and $z = 7.4 \times 10^{10}$.

    (b) Make y the subject of the formula.

12. $v^2 - 2gh = g\sqrt{c^2 + h^2}$

    (a) Make g the subject of the formula.

    (b) Find c in terms of v, g and h.

    (c) Evaluate v when $h = 124$, $g = 9.8$ and $c = 42.7$.

13. (a) $\dfrac{1}{a} = \dfrac{1}{b} + \dfrac{1}{3c}$, make c the subject.

    (b) Find the value of c when $a = 14$ and $b = 27$.

14. (a) $V = \dfrac{4}{3}\pi r^3$, express r in terms of V.

    (b) Find the value of r when $V = \dfrac{9\pi}{16}$.

15. (a) $p(q - t) = q^2(p - t)$, make t the subject.

    (b) Find the value of t when $p = 2$ and $q = -2$.

16. (a) $u = \dfrac{v}{6uw^2 - 1}$, find w in terms of u and v.

    (b) If $u = 0.352\,6$ and $v = 0.469\,3$, find the value of w, correct to three significant figures.

17. If $a = 3b$, $b = 4c$ and $c = 5d$, express a in terms of d. Find the values of a, b and c when $d = \frac{3}{4}$.

18. Solve the following equations.

(a) $x(x - 3) = 2x + 6$

(b) $3y(2y - 1) = 0$

(c) $(y + 4)^2 = 9$

(d) $(t - 1)(t + 1) = 48$

(e) $3x^2 - 75 = 0$

(f) $x^2 + 2x = 0$

(g) $(2x + 1)(x + 2) - 5 = 0$

(h) $(1 + 4x)(7 - 5x) = 0$

(i) $4x - 10x^2 = 0$

(j) $2x^2 + 5x = 12$

(k) $2y^2 - 5y - 7 = 0$

(l) $3(x - 1)^2 - 48 = 0$

(m) $1 - 3x - 18x^2 = 0$

(n) $(3x - 1)(x + 2) = 6$

(o) $x^2 = 9x$

(p) $10x - 2x^2 + 12 = 0$

19. Solve the following equations.

(a) $\dfrac{4}{v} = \dfrac{v}{9}$

(b) $\dfrac{1}{x^2} = 25$

(c) $\dfrac{10}{3y} + 1 = \dfrac{4}{y}$

(d) $\dfrac{6}{x} - \dfrac{3}{x + 1} = 2$

(e) $2 - m = \dfrac{3}{4m}$

(f) $10x - \dfrac{1}{x} = 3$

(g) $\dfrac{x}{x - 1} + \dfrac{x - 1}{x} = \dfrac{5}{2}$

(h) $\dfrac{3x}{2} = \dfrac{24}{x}$

(i) $\dfrac{11}{x - 7} = \dfrac{x - 7}{11}$

(j) $n + \dfrac{2}{3} = 9n^2$

(k) $\dfrac{m - 2}{m + 4} = m$

(l) $8x + x^2 = 0$

(m) $8x^2 + 1 = 9x$

(n) $\dfrac{9}{25}x^2 - 36 = 0$

20. Solve the following equations.

(a) (i) $5y - (3 - y) = 1$

(ii) $5y - (3 - y)^2 = 1$

(b) (i) $2(3 - x) = x$

(ii) $2(3 - x^2) = x$

(c) (i) $x(2x - 3) = 0$

(ii) $x(2x - 3) = 5$

(d) (i) $4y^2 - 16 = 0$

(ii) $4y^2 - 16y = 0$

(e) (i) $9x^2 = 49$

(ii) $9x^2 = 49x$

(f) (i) $25x^2 - 8 = 17$

(ii) $25x^2 - 8x = 17$

(iii) $25x^2 - 8 = 17x$

(g) (i) $(x + 1)^2 = 49$

(ii) $(2x - 3)^2 = 9$

(iii) $2(3x - 1)^2 = 8$

(h) (i) $a(2 - 18a) = 0$

(ii) $2 - 18a^2 = 0$

(i) (i) $(2y - 3)^2 = 0$

(ii) $(2y - 3)^2 = 3y$

(j) (i) $(2y + 1)(2y - 1) = 0$

(ii) $(2y + 1)(2y - 1) = 8$

(iii) $(2y + 3)(2y - 1) = 5$

(k) (i) $3x - 24 = 7(x - 2)$

(ii) $3x^2 - 24 = 7(x - 2)$

(l) (i) $5(4x + 3)(2x + 1) = 0$

(ii) $x(4x - 2)(5 - 6x) = 0$

(iii) $2x(1 - x)(2 + x) = 0$

(m) **(i)** $(5x - 15)(x - 3)(6 - 2x) = 0$
(ii) $(x - a)(x - b) \ldots (x - h) = 0$ where $a, b, \ldots h$ are constants.
(iii) $x(6x + 3)(4 - 8x)(-5 - 5x) = 0$
(n) **(i)** $3(-x + 1)(-x - 2) = 0$ **(ii)** $3(-x + 1)(-x - 2) = 12$

21.

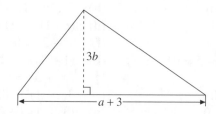

(a) Given that the area of the triangle is A square units, express a in terms of A and b.

(b) Hence find the value of a if the triangle has an area of 27 square units and a height of 6 units.

22. The perimeter, P, of the given sector is given by

$$P = 2r + \frac{\pi r x}{180}.$$

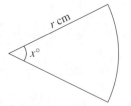

(a) Using $\pi = \frac{22}{7}$, find P when $r = 3.5$ and $x = 24$.

(b) Express r in terms of P, x and π. Hence evaluate r when $P = 80$ and $x = 140$.

23. **(a)** Express the sum, S, of any three consecutive even numbers in which n is the middle term, in terms of n. Hence find the sum of the three consecutive even numbers if the middle term is 46.

(b) Rewrite the formula so that you can use it to find the three consecutive even numbers when their sum is given. Use this to find the numbers when the sum is 828.

24. A car travels for 5 hours at u km/h and 3 hours at v km/h.
(a) If the average speed for the whole journey is S km/h, make S the subject of the formula.
(b) Find the average speed if $u = 60$ and $v = 80$.
(c) Express v in terms of S and u. Hence find the minimum value of v in order that the average speed for the whole journey is at least 70 km/h when $u = 55$.

25. A dealer bought x toys for \$270. He intended to sell each toy at a profit of \$10.
(a) If the selling price of each toy is \$$S$, find a formula connecting S and x.
(b) What is the selling price of each toy if he bought
(i) 9 toys,   **(ii)** 24 toys?
(c) Express x in terms of S and hence find the number of toys bought if the selling price of each toy is
(i) \$28,   **(ii)** \$32.50.

26. A rectangle has length $(2x + 3)$ cm and perimeter $(6x + 2)$ cm.
   (a) Find an expression, in terms of x, for the width of the rectangle.
   (b) Hence find a formula, in terms of x, for the area, A cm^2, of the rectangle.
   (c) Evaluate
      (i) A when $x = 5$,
      (ii) x when $A = 22$.
   (d) Hence write down the dimensions of the rectangle when the area of the rectangle is 22 cm^2.

27. The area of a rectangle is equal to the area of a square of side 4 cm. If the length of the rectangle is $(3x + 8)$ cm and its width is x cm, form an equation in x and show that it reduces to $3x^2 + 8x - 16 = 0$. Solve this equation for x and hence write down the dimensions of the rectangle.

28. The perimeter of a square of side $(x + 3)$ cm is equal to the area of another square of side x cm. Form an equation in x and show that it reduces to $x^2 - 4x - 12 = 0$. Solve this equation for x and hence write down the area of the larger square.

29. A square picture is to be mounted on a frame with a border of width 1 cm. If the area of the border is three times that of the area of the picture, find the length of the side of the picture.

30. A farmer encloses a rectangular piece of land having an area of 180 m^2 with a fence of total length 54 m. What are the dimensions of the land?

31. A rectangular lawn, 18 m wide and 20 m long, has a path of uniform width around it. If the area of the path is 168 m^2, find the width of the path.

32. I think of a positive integer. I square it and then minus five times of it. The result is 234. Find the number.

33. A man is three times as old as his son. Ten years ago, the sum of the square of their ages was 1 250. Find their present ages.

34. Danny is 7 years older than his brother. If the product of their ages is 120, find their ages.

35. A cyclist travels for $(x - 7)$ h at an average speed of $(2x + 3)$ km/h. Given that the distance travelled is 69 km, form an equation for the distance travelled in terms of x and show that it reduces to $2x^2 - 11x - 90 = 0$. Solve this equation and hence write down the average speed of the cyclist.

36. In the figure, *KLMN* is a trapezium.
    (a) Find, in terms of *x*, an expression for the area of the trapezium.
    (b) If the area of the trapezium is 15 cm², form an equation in *x* and show that it reduces to $2x^2 - 5x - 18 = 0$.
    (c) Solve this equation and find the length of *LM*.

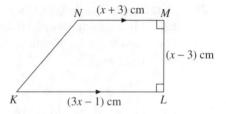

37. Three times a number subtracted from twice its square is the same as three times the number added to its square. What is the number?

38. The diagram represents a rectangular piece of paper *ABCD* which has been folded along *EF*, so that *C* has moved to *G*. *EC* = 3 cm, *FC* = 4 cm, *AB* = (*x* + 3) cm and *AD* = 3(*x* + 1) cm.
    (a) Calculate the area of triangle *ECF*.
    (b) Find an expression for the shaded area *ABFGED* in terms of *x* in the simplest form.
    (c) Given that the shaded area is 93 cm², show that $x^2 + 4x - 32 = 0$.
    (d) Solve the equation $x^2 + 4x - 32 = 0$ and hence write down the length of *AB*.

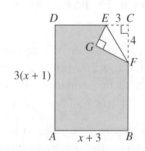

39. Three consecutive positive integers are such that the square of their sum exceeds the sum of their squares by 94. Find these three integers.
    (*Hint:* Use (*x* − 1), *x*, (*x* + 1).)

40. (a) In 1990, petrol cost 90¢ per litre. Calculate the number of litres of petrol that could be bought for $40.50.
    (b) In 1991, the price of petrol was increased by *x* cents per litre.
       Write down an expression, in terms of *x*, for
       (i) the cost in cents, of one litre of petrol in 1991.
       (ii) the number of litres of petrol that could be bought for $31.50 in 1991.
    (c) In 1992, the price was increased by a further *x* cents per litre. The quantity of petrol that cost $31.50 in 1991 now cost $36.00. Form an equation in *x* and solve it.

41. The base and the height of a triangle are of lengths 2*x* cm and (2*x* − 3) cm respectively.
    (a) Write down an expression for the area of the triangle in terms of *x*.
    (b) Given that the area of the triangle is 14 cm², form an equation in *x* and show that it reduces to $2x^2 - 3x - 14 = 0$.
    (c) Solve this equation and hence find the lengths of the base and the height.

42. A group of x people arrange to go on a picnic and share the total cost of $72.

    (a) Write down, in terms of x, how much each person should pay.

    (b) Shortly before the picnic, two others join the group, more food is added and the total cost now rises by $26. Write down, in terms of x, how much each person should now pay.

    (c) If the cost per person now is $1 more than what was originally expected, form an equation in x and show that it reduces to $x^2 - 24x + 144 = 0$.

    (d) Solve the equation $x^2 - 24x + 144 = 0$. Hence find the amount each member of the original group should pay.

43. A shopkeeper bought 12 toys at $\$x$ per toy. He proposed to sell each toy at a profit of $4 per toy.

    (a) Write down an expression, in terms of x, for the selling price of each toy.

    (b) He found that he was only able to sell x toys at this price. Write down an expression, in terms of x, for the total amount of money he received from selling these x toys.

    (c) Given that the shopkeeper received $77 altogether, form an equation in x and show that it reduces to $x^2 + 4x - 77 = 0$.

    (d) Solve the equation $x^2 + 4x - 77 = 0$. Hence find

        (i) the cost price of the 12 toys,

        (ii) the shopkeeper's loss.

CHAPTER 4 / Word Problems

1. A tea merchant mixes tea costing $7.40 per kg with tea costing $8.90 per kg in the ratio $3:2$. At what price must he sell the mixture to make a profit of 15%?

2. A salesman was paid an annual salary of $9 600. In addition, at the end of the year, he gets a bonus amounting to 8% of the value of his total annual sales.
   (a) If his total annual sales in the first year is $15 000, find his total income for the first year.
   (b) During the second year, he gets a 4% increase in his salary, find
       (i) his monthly salary,
       (ii) his total sales if his total income for that year is $11 904.

3. Only 60% of the voters in a certain constituency cast their votes. Of the votes cast, A received twice as much votes as B and B received one-third of what C received. If C received 8 000 votes more than B and assuming that no votes were spoilt,
   (a) how many votes did A receive,
   (b) how many voters were there in the constituency?

4. How many litres of milk (4.5% butterfat) must be mixed with 250 litres of skim milk (0% butterfat) to get low-fat milk (2% butterfat)?

5. 12 men can complete $\frac{5}{9}$ of a job in 5 days. How many more days are required to complete the job if 6 more men are added?

6. A dealer bought a car and sold it to Alex at a profit of $2 500. After one year, Alex sold it to Betty at a loss of 6%. If Betty paid $21 150 for the car, find the dealer's percentage profit.

7. A man bought 24 boxes of apples at $35.00 per box. There were 120 apples in each box. A total of 80 apples were found to be rotten and could not be sold. If he wanted to make a profit of $140, what should be the selling price of each apple?

8. The charge for 1 unit of electricity is increased from 6¢ to 6.25¢. If a household reduces its consumption by 1.6%, by what percentage will his electricity bill increase?
   By what percentage does a household need to reduce its consumption in order that the electricity bill remains unchanged?

9. A man's salary is increased from \$925 to \$1 036. Find the percentage increase. What would have been his new salary if the increase had been 16%?

10. Mr Chen and Mrs Chen each invested an equal sum of money in Bank A and Bank B respectively. Bank A pays 3% simple interest per annum, whilst Bank B pays $2\frac{3}{4}\%$ simple interest per annum. If at the end of two years, Mrs Chen's interest is \$30 less than Mr Chen's, how much money did each invest?

11. Two models, A and B, of a statue are made. A has a volume of 32 cm^3 and B has a volume of 56 cm^3. If models A and B have the same mass and the difference in the densities of the material used in making A and B is 1.8 g/cm^3, what is the mass of each model?

12. Alice needs to make a certain number of boxes. If she makes the boxes at a rate of 16 boxes per hour, she will take 2 hours longer than if she works at the rate of 18 boxes per hour. How many boxes does Alice need to make?

13. A certain number of matches are needed to fill 28 boxes (each box contains the same number of matches). When four matches fewer are put into each box, they are enough for 35 boxes. Find the total number of matches.

14. A man travels regularly between two cities. He takes $4\frac{2}{3}$ hours travelling at his usual speed. He finds that if he increases his speed by 3 km/h, he can reduce the time taken by $\frac{1}{3}$ hour. What is the distance between the two cities?

15. Two cars leave town at the same time and travel in opposite directions. The speed of one car is 68 km/h and the speed of the other car is 80 km/h. How far apart are the two cars after $3\frac{1}{4}$ hours?

16. Find the speed in m/s of a point on a bicycle rim, of diameter 84 cm, making 200 revolutions per minute.

17. The cost of petrol for a 240 km journey for a car which runs 12 km on each litre of petrol is \$23.80. What would be the cost of petrol for a 500 km journey in a car which runs 14 km on each litre of petrol?

18. A car takes 8 hours to travel between two cities at an average speed of 54 km/h. How much shorter will it take if the driver increases its average speed by 18 km/h?

19. If 3 women earn \$524 in 6 days, how much will 14 women earn in 9 days?

20. 12 men working 7 hours a day can finish a job in 6 days. How many more hours a day must 8 men work in order to finish the job in 7 days?

21. In a concert, the ratio of the number of female audience to the total number of audience is 4 : 7. If the number of audience is 1 022, how many are male audience?

22. *A, B* and *C* invest $3 500, $4 000 and $6 000 respectively in a business. If the profit from the business is $1 620, what should be the share for *A*?

23. A packet of biscuits was divided into two portions in the ratio 7 : 4. The smaller portion was divided into three portions in the ratio 3 : 1 : 4. If the smallest of these portions had 18 biscuits, what was the total number of biscuits in the packet?

24. A merchant spent $2 250 in buying 1 000 articles. He fixed the selling price to allow him a profit of 20% on his cost, and sold $\frac{4}{5}$ of the articles at this price. He then reduced his selling price by half and sold the remainder of his stocks at the new price. Calculate his new profit as a percentage of his expenditure.

25. Two men *A* and *B* can complete a job in 10 days. If *A* alone can do it in 15 days, how long will *B* take to do it himself?

26. A car uses petrol at an average rate of 8 litres per 100 km. The owner spends $30 on petrol costing $1.20 per litre. Calculate, correct to the nearest kilometre, the distance his car can travel on this amount of petrol.

27. If 12 men can dig 35 holes in 14 days,
  (a) how many men are needed to dig 35 holes in 8 days,
  (b) how many days would it take 12 men to dig 30 holes?

28. **(a)** By paying $3 000 for a motorcycle, a buyer was paying only 60% of the price listed. Calculate the list price.
  (b) If the buyer chose to pay in 18 monthly instalments of $150 each, find the difference between the cash price and the hire purchase price if an initial deposit of $600 was paid. Express this difference as a percentage of the cash price.

29. Calculate
  (a) the cost of fifty $8\frac{1}{2}$ p stamps,
  (b) the number of $6\frac{1}{2}$ p stamps that can be bought for £16.90.

30. Mary works in a fastfood restaurant. She is paid $2.50 an hour on weekdays and $3·50 an hour on weekends. The table shows the number of hours she works in a week.

Mon	Tue	Wed	Thur	Fri	Sat	Sun
x	$4\frac{1}{2}$	4	5	$5\frac{1}{2}$	$6\frac{1}{2}$	$5\frac{1}{2}$

   (a) If she earned $102 altogether, how many hours did she work on Monday?
   (b) She spends $0.90 on transport and $1.30 on lunch every day. What percentage of her income will she save in one week?

31. Andy drives at a speed of 75 km/h.
   (a) How far will he travel in 1 hour and 28 minutes?
   (b) How many minutes will he take to reach a town 23.5 km away?
   (c) Express this speed in m/s.

32. A bank pays 3% interest per annum on savings and 4% interest per annum on fixed deposits. Mabel has $2 500 in her savings account and $2 000 as fixed deposits in the bank. How much interest will she get altogether at the end of $2\frac{1}{2}$ years?

33. In a certain country, the tax which a married man with children has to pay is calculated as follows:
   From his total income, a marriage allowance of $4 000 and also an allowance of $1 000 for each child are deducted. The remainder is his taxable income. On the first $15 000, tax at the rate of 15% is charged. On the rest of his taxable income, 20% is charged.
   (a) A married man with two children has a total income of $20 000. How much tax does he pay?
   (b) In the following year, the man has a third child and his income is now $25 000. Calculate the percentage increase in the tax he pays, giving your answer to one decimal place.

34. The density of a certain metal is 2.4 g/cm^3.
   (a) Find the volume, in cm^3, of 0.48 kg of the metal.
   (b) Express this density in kg/m^3.

35. **(a)** If pages 6 and 19 are on the same (double) sheet of newspaper, which other pages are on the same sheet? How many pages does the newspaper have altogether?
   (b) If pages 20 and 29 are on the same (double) sheet of a magazine, which other pages are on the same sheet? How many pages does the magazine have altogether?

36. If all the stars stand for the same number, complete the following.

(a) $\dfrac{\star}{\star} - \dfrac{\star}{8} = \dfrac{\star}{24}$

(b) $\dfrac{\star}{6} + \dfrac{\star}{12} = \dfrac{\star}{\star}$

37. You are given a piece of wood measuring 8 cm by 18 cm. The wood is cut into two pieces as shown in the figure on the right. The pieces are then rearranged to form a square.

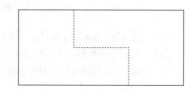

(a) Draw a diagram to show how the two pieces are arranged to form the square.

(b) Write down the dimensions of the two pieces on the figure above, as well as on the square drawn.

(c) Find the difference between the perimeters of the rectangle and the square.

38. The diagram shows two squares. One square is inscribed inside, the other is circumscribed in a given circle. If the smaller square has area 4 square units, what is the area of the larger square?

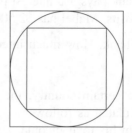

39. Two identical squares overlap as shown, with one corner of one square at the centre of the other square. Find the area of the overlapping region.

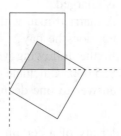

40. (a) Some of the digits in the following multiplications are missing. Can you find all the missing digits?

(i)
$$
\begin{array}{r}
\star\,6\,\star \\
\times \qquad 7 \\
\hline
\star\,1\,\star\,3 \\
\end{array}
$$

(ii)
$$
\begin{array}{r}
\star\,7 \\
\times \quad \star \\
\hline
4\,\star\,3 \\
\end{array}
$$

(iii)
$$
\begin{array}{r}
6\,\star \\
\times \quad \star \\
\hline
3\,\star\,4 \\
\end{array}
$$

(b) Can you replace the $\star$'s with the digits 1, 2, 3 and 4 using each digit once? How many different solutions are there?

$$
\begin{array}{r}
\star \\
\star\,)\,\overline{\star\ \ \star} \\
\end{array}
$$

(c) Can you replace the ☆'s with the digits 1, 2, 3, 4 and 5 using each digit once? How many different solutions are there?

$$\begin{array}{r} ☆\,☆ \\ \times\quad ☆ \\ \hline ☆\,☆ \end{array}$$

41. Substitute a digit for each letter so as to make the following additions true. (The same letter stands for the same digit. Different letters stand for different digits.)

(a)
$$\begin{array}{r} FOUR \\ +\ ONE \\ \hline FIVE \end{array}$$

(b)
$$\begin{array}{r} ONE \\ +\ ONE \\ \hline TWO \end{array}$$

(c)
$$\begin{array}{r} TWO \\ \times\ TWO \\ \hline FOUR \end{array}$$

42. You have a 100 m*l* cup and a 70 m*l* cup.
    (a) How can you get exactly 90 m*l* of water?
    (b) How can you get exactly 40 m*l* of water?

43. 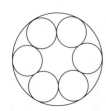 The outer circle has radius 1. Each of the six identical smaller circles touches its two neighbours and the big circle. What is the radius of the largest circle that will fit in the central hole?

44. (a) Each amoeba divides into two separate amoebas once every hour. If we start with just one amoeba, how many will there be at the end of 1 hour, 2 hours? 3 hours, and so on? Complete the following table. (Mathematical amoebas never die!)

Time (hours)	Start	1	2	3	4	5	. . . .	10
No. of amoebas	1						. . . .	

(b) Rabbits come in breeding pairs. They start to breed at the age of two months. They then produce one breeding pair of rabbits every month. If we start with one newly born pair of rabbits, how many pairs will there be at the end of one month, two months, three months, and so on? Complete the table. (Mathematical rabbits never die!)

Time (months)	Start	1	2	3	4	5	. . . . . .	10
No. of breeding pairs	1						. . . . . .	

Note: The number sequence obtained in (a) is the sequence of powers of two.
       The number sequence obtained in (b) is the sequence of Fibonacci numbers.

45. (a) The following pattern of numbers is called the Pascal's triangle. Make a Pascal's triangle of your own. Fill in the numbers in the first nine rows. (The number in the middle of the ninth row should be 70.)

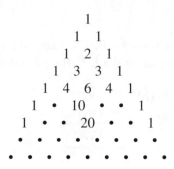

```
          1
        1   1
      1   2   1
    1   3   3   1
  1   4   6   4   1
1  •  10  •   •  1
1  •  •  20  •  •  1
  •  •  •  •  •  •  •
    •  •  •  •  •  •
```

(b) The following pattern of numbers is called the harmonic triangle. Complete the pattern up to the seventh row.

$$1$$

$$\frac{1}{2} \quad \frac{1}{2}$$

$$\frac{1}{3} \quad \frac{1}{6} \quad \frac{1}{3}$$

$$\frac{1}{4} \quad \frac{1}{12} \quad \frac{1}{12} \quad \frac{1}{4}$$

$$\frac{1}{5} \quad \frac{1}{20} \quad • \quad • \quad \frac{1}{5}$$

$$• \quad \frac{1}{30} \quad • \quad • \quad • \quad •$$

$$• \quad • \quad • \quad • \quad • \quad •$$

46. Complete the table below to find the maximum number of chords that can be formed when there are N points on the circle.

No. of points, N, on the circle	1	2	3	4	5	6	7	......	10	50
No. of chords formed	0	1						......		

Can you find a formula for calculating the number of chords, C, from the number of points, N?

47. Which of these two numbers is bigger
$$100^2 - 99^2 + 98^2 - 97^2 + 96^2 - \ldots - 1^2$$
or $100 + 99 + 98 + 97 + 96 + \ldots + 1$?

48. (a) In an incubator of 400 eggs, it is expected that 85% should hatch. Find the number of chicks expected to hatch.

(b) If 389 eggs are hatched, calculate the percentage which did not hatch.

(c) On a certain day, a stallholder sold 130 chicks which was 4% more than he had expected. Calculate the number of chicks he had expected to sell.

49. A shopkeeper buys and sells three different articles.

(a) He buys the first article for $40 and sells it for $52. What is his percentage profit?

(b) The second article costs him $26 and he sells it at a profit of 28%. How much does he sell it for?

(c) (i) The shopkeeper makes a loss of 12% when he sells the third article for $286. How much did he pay for it?

(ii) How much must he sell the article in order to make a 12% profit?

50. A bus travels at 42 km/h and arrives at its destination half an hour late. If it travels at 48 km/h, it will arrive at the same destination half an hour earlier. Find the length of the journey.

51. A man travelled 20 km in $2\frac{3}{4}$ hours. He cycled part of the way at 10 km/h and walked the rest at 4 km/h.

(a) How far did he cycle?

(b) How long did he take to walk the rest of the journey?

1. A restaurant owner pays a waiter an amount of A per week. The amount is made up of a basic wage of $60 plus 11 cents for each of the n customers he serves. The formula connecting A and n in this case is

$$A = 60 + \frac{11n}{100}.$$

   (a) Calculate the amount of money the waiter received in a week when he served 240 customers. [1]

   Ans _____

   (b) At the end of another week, the waiter received $115.
   (i) Express n in terms of A. [2]
   (ii) How many customers did he serve? [1]

   Ans (i) _____

   (ii) _____

(c) The owner of the restaurant decides to decrease the waiter's basic wage to $45 but to increase the pay per customer to 17 cents. Write down the new formula connecting *A* and *n*. [2]

Ans _____

(d) Find the number of customers the waiter would have to serve in a week for him to receive the same amount of money whichever formula is used. [4]

Ans _____

2. A farmer has 35 kg of food for his 40 cattle to last 25 days.
   (a) If he buys 10 more cattle, how long will the same amount of food last? [3]
   (b) If he buys 14 kg more of food, how many days longer will the food last for the 40 cattle? [3]

Ans (a) _____

(b) _____

3. A cyclist is travelling from A to C in a remote part of the country. He travels for 50 km at a constant speed of x km/h, until he reaches point B, where his bicycle chain breaks. He then walks for 6 km from B to C at a constant speed of $(x - 16)$ km/h.

(a) Write down, in terms of x, the time taken for his journey
  (i) from A to B,
  (ii) from B to C. [2]

Ans (i) _____

(ii) _____

(b) Given that the total time for the whole journey from A to C is 4 hours, write down an equation in x and show that it reduces to
$$x^2 - 30x + 200 = 0.$$
[4]

Ans _____

34

(c) Solve the equation $x^2 - 30x + 200 = 0$. Hence find the time, in hours and minutes, the cyclist would have taken if he had completed the whole journey by bicycle at the original constant speed. [4]

Ans _____

4. Mr Wang buys 30 *l* of petrol at a certain price. He finds that if he had bought some cheaper petrol costing 4.4 cents less per litre, he could have $31\frac{1}{9}$ *l* for the same amount of money. What is the price per litre of the dearer petrol? [8]

Ans _____

5. A man has a sum of money to be given to his wife, his son and his three grandchildren in the ratio 6 : 3 : 2 respectively. His three grandchildren, ages 4, 5 and 7 years are to share the smallest portion of money in the ratio of their ages. If the eldest grandchild gets $975 more than the youngest grandchild, find the sum of money. [5]

Ans _____

6. The selling price of a washing machine is $435.
   (a) Calculate the cost price if the seller earns a 45% profit. [3]

Ans _____

(b) Samuel receives a 4% commission on every washing machine sold. How much commission does he earn if he sells 12 washing machines? [2]

Ans _____

(c) Customers who hold a privileged card are given a 5% discount. How much does such customers have to pay for a washing machine? [2]

Ans _____

(d) Buyers can also choose to pay for a washing machine by hire purchase which consists of an initial downpayment of $80 and 6 monthly instalments of $70 per month. Express the difference between the cash price and the hire purchase price as a percentage of the cash price. [4]

Ans _____

CHAPTER 5 / Graphs I

1. **(a)** Using a scale of 2 cm to 1 unit on each axis, plot and label the points represented by the following ordered pairs of numbers.

    $$A(0, -1), \ B(0, 7), \ C(5, 4).$$

    Join the points with straight lines and identify the geometrical shape obtained.
    (b) Draw on your graph the line of symmetry of figure ABC and write down its equation.
    (c) Find the area of figure ABC.
    (d) Draw the line $x = 2$ on your diagram and write down the coordinates of the points of intersection of the line and the figure.

2. A calculator is programmed under a certain rule in each of the following cases. The table shows some of the values of x and the corresponding values of y. Find the rule connecting x and y in each case. Hence complete each of the following tables.

    (a)

x	1	2	3	4	5	13	50
y	3	5	7	9	11		

    (b)

x	1	2	3	4	5	13	50
y	1.5	3	4.5	6	7.5		

    (c)

x	1	2	3	4	5	13	50
y	1	4	9	16	25		

3. **(a)** Taking 3 cm to represent 1 unit on the x-axis and 2 cm to represent 1 unit on the y-axis, draw the axes for values of x in the range $-2 \leqslant x \leqslant 3$ and for values of y in the range $-1 \leqslant y \leqslant 8$.
    (b) On the same axes, draw the graph for each of the following equations, using two ordered pairs with values of x and y in the given range.
    (i) $y = 3x + 4$
    (ii) $3x - y - 1 = 0$
    (iii) $2x + y - 4 = 0$
    (iv) $7x - 2y = 0$
    (v) $y = -x$

(c) Linear equations are of the form $y = mx + c$, where m and c are constants. By writing each of the equations in (b) in the form $y = mx + c$, write down the values of m and c for each case.

(d) From the graphs, what do you notice about each of the following?
(i) Graphs with the same values of m.
(ii) Graphs with a greater numerical value of m.
(iii) Graphs with the same value of c.
(iv) Graphs with the value of c equals zero.
(v) Graphs with negative values of m.

4. (a) Study the graphs of the vertical and horizontal lines below and write down the equations for lines a, b, c and d. Write down also the coordinates of the points A to F.

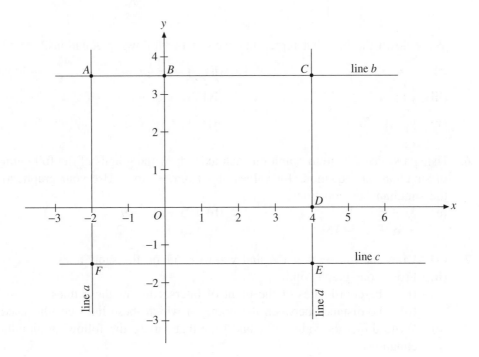

(b) Draw, on the axes above, the graphs of the following equations.
(i) $y - 2 = 0$
(ii) $2x - 1 = 0$
(iii) $x = 0$
(iv) $y = 0$
(c) (i) What is the equation representing the x-axis?
(ii) What is the equation representing the y-axis?

5.

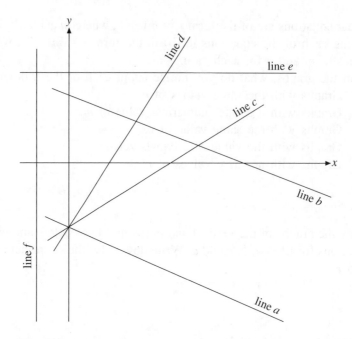

Write down the line that represents each of the following equations.

(i) $x = -2$

(ii) $y = -\dfrac{1}{2}x + 3$

(iii) $y = 4x - 2$

(iv) $y = 3x - 2$

(v) $y - 4 = 0$

(vi) $y = -\dfrac{1}{2}x - 2$

6.   Using a scale of 2 cm to 1 unit on each axis, draw the graphs of the following pairs of simultaneous equations for values of x from -3 to 3. Use your graphs to solve the simultaneous equations.

(a) $3x + 5y = 9$
      $-5x + 2y = 16$

(b) $3x - 2y = 9$
      $2x + y = -2$

7.   **(a)**   Draw the lines $y = x + 4$ and $y = 6x - 11$ on the same axes.

(b)   From your graph, find

   (i)   the coordinates of the point of intersection of these lines,

   (ii)   the distance between the points at which these lines cut the y-axis.

(c)   Write down the value of x and of y that satisfy the following simultaneous equations.

$$x - y = -4$$
$$6x - y = 11$$

8.   Obtain graphically the solutions of the following simultaneous equations.
$$2x + 7y = 6$$
$$x - 5y = 3$$

9.   Draw the graphs of $y = 2x + 1$ and $2y = 4x + 5$. Are you able to find the point of intersection of the graphs $y = 2x + 1$ and $2y = 4x + 5$? Give reasons for your answer.

10. The equations of the sides of a quadrilateral *ABCD* are as follows:

$AB : 4y + x = 20$

$BC : x = 0$

$CD : y + 2x = 2$

$AD : 3y = 4x - 4$

Find the coordinates of *A*, *B*, *C* and *D* by a graphical method.

11. Which ordered pair(s) satisfy the equation $y = 2x - 5$?
   (a) $A(2, -1)$
   (b) $B(3, -2)$
   (c) $C(0, 5)$
   (d) $D(-2, -9)$
   (e) $E(4, -3)$

12. Calculate the coordinates of the point of intersection of the lines
   (a) $y = 2x - 1$ and $y = x + 3$,
   (b) $y = x - 3$ and the *x*-axis,
   (c) $y = 5x + 4$ and the *y*-axis,
   (d) $y = 3x - 1$ and $x = 2$.

13.

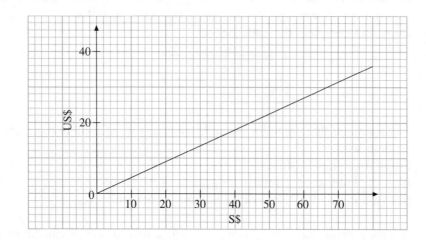

   (a) How much Singapore dollars can you get from US$1?
   (b) Would S$65 be enough to buy a coat costing US$38?
   (c) A moneychanger offers to change a S$50 note for a US$20 note. Is this profitable? Why?
   (d) What is the difference, in Singapore dollars, between S$40 and US$32?
   (e) Mr Li went on a tour and he has US$16 left after the tour. He wanted to exchange the money for Singapore dollars. How many Singapore dollars would he get?

14. The relationship between Fahrenheit (°F) scale and Celsius (°C) scale of a thermometer is given by $F = \dfrac{9}{5}C + 32$. Draw a graph of °F against °C to show the relationship.

From your graph, convert

(a) 77°F and 20°F to °C,   (b) −3°C and 37°C to °F.

15. A pyramid has a base area of 8 cm^2 and a height of x cm.

(a) Express the volume, y, of the pyramid in terms of x.

(b) Copy and complete the table below.

x (cm)	0	
y (cm^3)		80

(c) Plot a straight line graph for the table with the following scales:

2 cm on the x-axis represents 5 cm
1 cm on the y-axis represents 5 cm^3

(d) Use your graph to find the following:

(i) The volume of the pyramid if the height is 23 cm.

(ii) The height of the pyramid with a volume of 35 cm^3.

16. (a) A solid of volume 40 cm^3 weighs 60 g. If x cm^3 of a solid made of the same material weigh y g, find the equation connecting x and y.

(b) Copy and complete the table below.

x (cm^3)	0	
y (g)		30

(c) Plot a straight line graph for the table using a scale of 2 cm to represent 5 units on both axes.

(d) From your graph, estimate

(i) the volume of a solid with a mass of 18 g,

(ii) the mass of a solid with a volume of 6.5 cm^3.

17. (a) A square prism has a height of 3 cm and a base of side x cm. Show that its total surface area, y, is given by $y = 2x^2 + 12x$.

(b) Copy and complete the following table of values.

x	0	1	2	3	4	5	6
y	0	14		54	80		144

Hence plot the graph of y against x, using a scale of 2 cm to represent 1 unit on the x-axis and 1 cm to represent 10 units on the y-axis.

42

(c) From your graph, find
  (i) the value of x when the total surface area is 70 cm^2,
  (ii) the area of the prism with a base of side 1.5 cm.
(d) A second prism has a height of x cm and a base of side 4 cm.
  (i) Find the total surface area of the second prism in terms of x.
  (ii) By drawing a suitable straight line, estimate the value of x for which both prisms have the same area.

18. The graph shows the cost, in dollars, for units of household electricity. Use the graph to estimate
  (a) the cost of
    (i) the first 300 units,
    (ii) the first 120 units,
  (b) the number of units bought for
    (i) $30,
    (ii) $18,
  (c) the cost per unit for the
    (i) first 100 units,
    (ii) next 100 units.

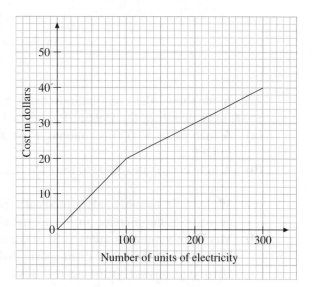

19.

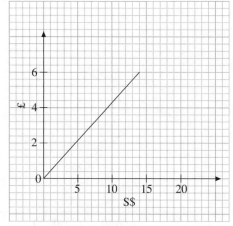

The graphs show the rates of exchange between Pounds sterling (£) and Singapore dollars (S$) and between Japanese yen and Singapore dollars.
Use your graphs to estimate
  (a) the number of dollars in £6,   **(b)** the number of pounds in S$7,
  (c) the number of yen in S$13,   **(d)** the number of pounds in 80 yen.

20.

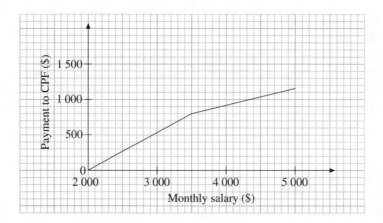

The graph shows the contributions made by those earning between \$2 000 and \$5 000 per month to the Central Provident Fund (CPF).

(a) A man earns \$3 000 per month. Estimate, to the nearest \$5, his contribution to CPF.

(b) A lady contributes \$900 to the CPF. Estimate, to the nearest \$10, her monthly salary.

(c) Mr David's monthly salary increases from \$3 100 to \$4 100. Estimate, to the nearest \$5, the increase in his contribution to the CPF.

(d) Mrs Chen's monthly salary is \$1 800 and Mr Chen's monthly salary is \$4 400. How much of their total earnings are deducted for CPF contributions monthly? Give your answer to the nearest \$10.

21.

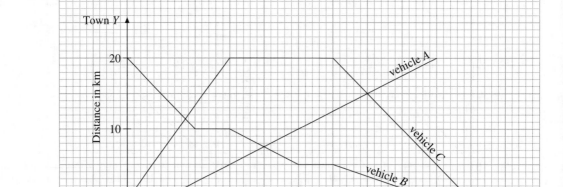

The travel graphs above represent the journeys of three vehicles between town X and town Y which are 20 km apart. Study the graphs carefully and answer the questions.

(a) Which vehicle travelled from town Y to town X?

(b) Which vehicle travelled at a constant speed throughout?

(c) When did vehicle A begin its journey and for how long did it travel?

(d) What was the average speed of vehicle A?

(e) How many times did vehicle B rest and for how long altogether?

(f) What was the average speed of vehicle B in the last part of its journey?

(g) When did vehicle B travel the fastest?

(h) When and where did vehicle C stop and for how long?

(i) What was the total distance travelled by vehicle C?

(j) What was the average speed of vehicle C for the whole journey?

(k) When and where did vehicle A meet vehicles B and C?

(l) How far were vehicles A, B and C from their starting points at time 08 13?

(m) At what time was vehicle B 3 km from its destination?

(n) How many minutes did it take vehicle A to travel 17 km?

22.

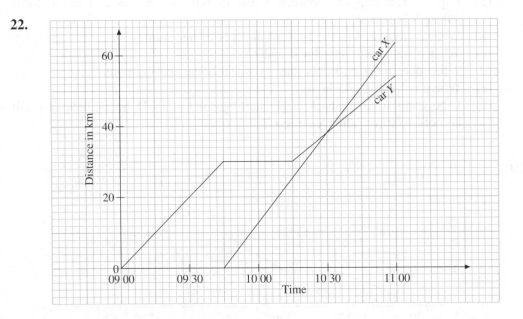

The distance-time graph of two cars X and Y are represented by the graph above.

(a) Is the speed of car X uniform throughout the journey? Give a reason for your answer.

(b) Did car Y rest at any part of the journey? Give a reason for your answer.

(c) Calculate the average speeds of car X and car Y for the whole journey.

(d) When and where did car X overtake car Y?

(e) How far is car Y from the starting point at 10 15?

(f) Where was car X after travelling for half an hour?

(g) How long does it take car Y to complete the last 8 km of its journey?

(h) At what time was car Y 24 km from its destination?

45

23.

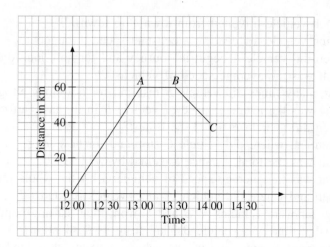

The graph shows the distance of a motorist from his starting point over a period of 2 hours.

(a) Explain what happens between A and B. What is the speed of the motorist during this period?

(b) What is his speed in the first 60 minutes of his journey?

(c) What is his speed between B and C?

(d) When does he start on his journey towards the starting point?

(e) Where is he at 13 45 hours?

(f) If he wants to arrive back at his starting point at 14 45 hours, how fast will he need to travel after leaving C?

24.

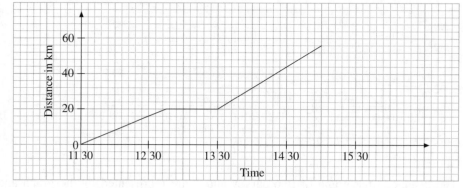

The diagram above shows the travel graph for a cyclist starting at 11 30 and completing his journey at 15 00.

(a) How far did he travel?

(b) What is his average speed for the first 75 minutes?

(c) Calculate the average speed of the cyclist for the whole journey.

(d) At 11 45, another cyclist starts from a place 56 km from the starting point of the first cyclist and travels at a constant speed of 14 km/h towards the first cyclist. Draw the travel graph of the second cyclist on the grid.

25.

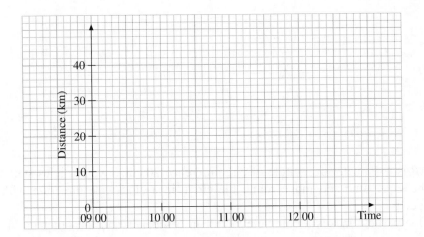

A cyclist set out at 09 00 for a destination 40 km away. He cycled at a speed of 15 km/h until 10 30, when he rested for half an hour. He then completed his journey at a speed of 20 km/h.

On the given axes, draw the distance-time graph to represent the journey and use your graph to estimate the time at which the cyclist reached his destination. *(C)*

26. The distance from X to Y is 12 km. A man leaves X at 12 00 and walks to Y at a steady speed of 6 km/h. A second man leaves Y at 12 00 and cycles to X at a constant speed, passing the first man at 12 30.

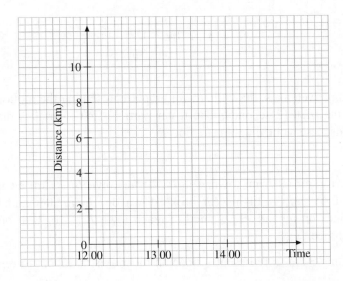

On the grid provided, draw the distance-time graph for each man. *(C)*

27.

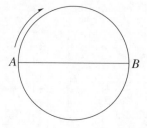

AB is a diameter of a circle of circumference 20 cm. Two particles start from A at the same time and move round the circle in a clockwise direction with constant speeds.

One particle makes a complete circuit in 6 seconds and the other in 24 seconds.

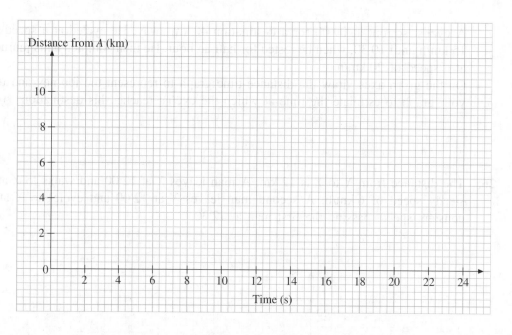

Using the given axes, draw the travel graph representing the motion of each particle during the first 12 seconds. The faster particle first overtakes the other one after t seconds. Use your diagram to find t.

(C)

28. A motorist set out from town A at 08 20 for town B, 70 km away. He drove at a speed of 45 km/h until his car broke down one hour later and he had to spend 30 minutes on repairs. He wanted to reach town B at 10 30 to be just in time for a conference.

(a) Using 3 cm to represent $\frac{1}{2}$ hour on the x-axis and 2 cm to represent 10 km on the y-axis, draw the distance-time graph to represent the journey.

(b) At what speed must he drive in order to be just in time for the conference?

(c) What was the average speed for the whole journey, to the nearest km/h?

29.

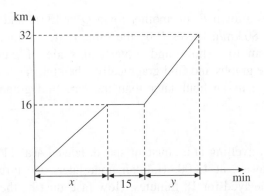

The diagram shows the distance-time graph for a car which travels a distance of 16 km in x minutes at an average speed of v km/h. The car stops to rest for 15 minutes before it goes for a further 16 km at an average speed of $\frac{3}{2}v$ km/h. The total time for the journey is 90 minutes. Find

(a) the ratio $\dfrac{x}{y}$,

(b) the value of x,

(c) the average speed for the whole journey.

30. Two cyclists, A and B, start a 30 km journey at 08 00. Cyclist A maintains an average speed of 20 km/h for the first half of an hour and then stops for a rest. Subsequently he continues his journey at an average speed of 40 km/h, arriving at his destination at 10 00. Cyclist B cycles without stopping at an average speed of V km/h for the whole journey and arrives at his destination at the same time as cyclist A.

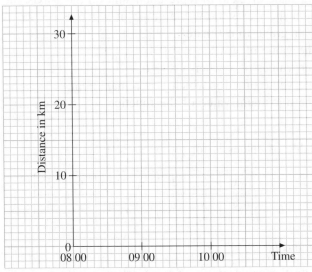

(a) Draw the travel graphs of cyclists A and B on the axes provided.

(b) State, in minutes, the duration of cyclist A's rest.

(c) Find the value of V.

(d) When and where does cyclist B pass cyclist A?

31. A bus leaves a town P for another town Q at 13 00 and travels at 60 km/h. A car travelling at 80 km/h leaves P by the same route an hour later. Using a horizontal scale of 2 cm to 1 hour and a vertical scale of 2 cm to 100 km, draw the distance-time graphs and find graphically when the car overtakes the bus. If the bus arrives at Q half an hour later than the car, find graphically, the distance from P to Q.

32. A motorist, travelling at a constant speed, leaves A at 11 00, intending to arrive at B, 100 km away, at 13 00. Half an hour later, one tyre has a puncture and the motorist is delayed for 18 minutes. How fast must he then travel in order to reach B on time? At what time will he meet a cyclist who leaves B at 11 45 for A at a constant speed of 20 km/h? Illustrate your answer using a distance-time graph.

33. Two men start moving towards each other at the same time. If they are 32 km apart and one is cycling at 20 km/h and the other walking at 7 km/h, how long will it take them to pass each other? At what time are they 5 km apart? Illustrate your answer using a distance-time graph.

34. Copy and complete the following table for $y = 6 + x - 2x^2$.

(a)

x	-3	-2	-1	0	1	2	3
y	-15		3		5		-9

(b) Using a scale of 2 cm to represent 1 unit on the x-axis and 1 cm to represent 1 unit on the y-axis, draw the graph of $y = 6 + x - 2x^2$ for $-3 \leqslant x \leqslant 3$.

(c) Use your graph to estimate
   (i) the value of y when $x = 0.4$,
   (ii) the values of x when $y = -6$,
   (iii) the value of x for which y is a maximum,
   (iv) the maximum value of the function $y = 6 + x - 2x^2$.

35. The given table of values is for $y = x^2 - 5x + 5$.

x	0	1	2	3	4	5
y	5	a	-1	b	1	5

(a) Find a and b.

(b) Calculate the value of $x^2 - 5x + 5$ when $x = 2\frac{1}{2}$.

(c) Using a scale of 2 cm to 1 unit on each axis, draw the graph of $y = x^2 - 5x + 5$ for $0 \leqslant x \leqslant 5$.

(d) Use your graph to solve the equation $x^2 - 5x + 5 = 0$.

(e) Find, from your graph,
    (i)   the value of y when $x = 3.3$,
    (ii) the values of x when $y = 2.8$.
(f) Write down the minimum value of the function $y = x^2 - 5x + 5$.
(g) Write down the value of x where the minimum occurs.
(h) Draw the line of symmetry of your graph.
(i) Write down the equation of the line of symmetry.

36.

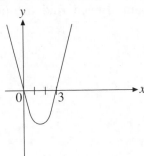

If the equation of the curve in the diagram is $y = x^2 + bx + c$, find the value of b and of c.   (C)

37. The curve $y = px^3 + 8$ intersects the y-axis at A and passes through the point $(-2, -32)$.
    (a) Write down the coordinates of A.
    (b) Calculate the value of p.   (C)

38.

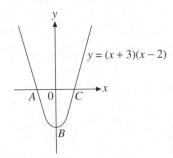

The curve $y = (x + 3)(x - 2)$ cuts the x-axis at the points A and C and the y-axis at B.
    (a) Write down the coordinates of the points A, B and C.
    (b) Find the equation of the line of symmetry of the curve.   (C)

39.

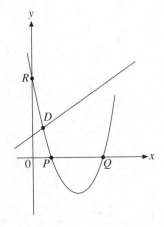

The diagram shows a sketch of part of the graph of $y = (x - 2)(x - 6)$. The curve cuts the x-axis at P and Q and the y-axis at R.
    (a) Write down the coordinates of P, Q and R.
    (b) The coordinates of the point D are $(1, d)$. Given that the point D lies on the curve, calculate the value of d.
    (c) Given also that the straight line $y = x + k$ passes through D, calculate the value of k.   (C)

40. Answer the whole of this question on a sheet of graph paper.
A quadrilateral $ABCD$ has vertices $(-4, 0)$, $(-2, 7)$, $(4, 7)$ and $(6, 0)$ respectively.

(a) Using a scale of 1 cm to represent 1 unit on each axis, draw and label the quadrilateral $ABCD$.

(b) What type of quadrilateral is $ABCD$?

(c) Draw on your graph the line of symmetry of the quadrilateral $ABCD$. Write down the equation of this line of symmetry.

(d) Find the area of the quadrilateral $ABCD$.

(e) Draw the line $2x + 3y = 6$ on your diagram. Hence find the point of intersection of this line and the side AB.

CHAPTER 6

Simultaneous Linear Equations

Solve the following simultaneous equations for x and y.

1. $5x - 4y = 40$
$x + 4y = -16$

2. $6x + 7y = 10$
$4x - 3y = -1$

3. $x - 6y = 17$
$5x + 3y = 2\frac{1}{2}$

4. $3x + 2y = 0$
$x - y = 2.5$

5. $x = 3y - 2$
$9y = 4x - 7$

6. $2y + 3x = 0$
$2x - 26 = 3y$

7. $3x - 4y = -6$
$2x - \frac{4}{3}y = 4$

8. $13 + 2y = 9x$
$3y = 7x$

9. $8x + 3y = -4$
$\frac{1}{2}x - y = -5$

10. $7(x - y) = 6x - 1$
$4(x + 1) = y + 3$

11. $4y = x + 1$
$2y = \frac{2x + 3}{2}$

12. $\frac{x}{3} + \frac{y}{2} = 4$
$\frac{2x}{3} - \frac{y}{6} = 1$

13. $1.2x - 0.8y = 0.4$
$y + 0.1x = 0.3$

14. $5x + 7y - 17 = 0$
$27 - 7y - 3x = 0$

15. $4(2x - y + 3) = 0$
$2(x + y) - 3(x - y) = 6$

16. $\frac{x}{3} + \frac{y}{4} = 3x - 7y - 37 = 0$

17. $\frac{1}{5}(x - 3) = \frac{1}{2}(y - 7)$
$11x = 13y$

18. $\frac{1}{3}x - \frac{5}{9}y = -1$
$0.4x + 0.5y = 2.3$

19. $2x - y + 1 = 3x - y = \dfrac{1}{2}$

20. $\dfrac{x+1}{y+2} = \dfrac{2}{3}$

$\dfrac{x-2}{y-1} = \dfrac{1}{3}$

Solve the following simultaneous equations.

21. $0.8x - 3y = -6$

$1.2x + 0.5y = 3$

22. $6(x + y) - 4(x + 1) = -1$

$\dfrac{1}{2}(4x - 9y) + \dfrac{1}{3}(x + 4) = 1$

23. $\dfrac{1}{3}(2x - y) - \dfrac{1}{2}(3x - 1) = -5$

$2(y - x) = 3(4x - y) + 3$

24. $\dfrac{x + 4y}{6} = y$

$\dfrac{3x + 6y}{2} = 4x - 1$

25. $\dfrac{x - y}{3} = \dfrac{2x + y}{2}$

$\dfrac{x + y + 5}{2} = \dfrac{3x}{5}$

26. $6x - 4y + 1 = 9x - 8y + 2 = 4y - 3x$

27. $3\dfrac{1}{3}x - 3y = 2\dfrac{5}{6}$

$2\dfrac{1}{4}y - 1\dfrac{1}{9}x = -1\dfrac{1}{12}$

28. $x = 3 + 4y$

$y = 2 + 3x$

29. $11x + 3y + 7 = 0$

$2x + 5y - 21 = 0$

30. $\dfrac{x+1}{3} + y = 8$

$x - \dfrac{y+1}{3} = -4$

31. $\dfrac{2x - 3y}{4} = \dfrac{3x - 2y}{5} = 7.5$

32. Using the substitution $u = \dfrac{1}{x}$ and $v = \dfrac{1}{y}$, solve the following simultaneous equations.

(a) $\dfrac{1}{x} + \dfrac{2}{y} = -1$

$\dfrac{3}{x} + \dfrac{5}{y} = 2$

(b) $\dfrac{1}{3x} + \dfrac{4}{5y} = 0$

$\dfrac{1}{2x} - \dfrac{2}{15y} = \dfrac{10}{3}$

33. Find the point of intersection of the following pairs of lines.

(a) $y = 3x - 4$

$2x + 3y + 1 = 0$

(b) $\dfrac{x}{5} + \dfrac{y}{3} = 1$

$2x - 5y = 20$

34. A concert was attended by x adults and y children. Each of the y children paid $3 which was $\frac{3}{4}$ of what each of the adults paid. Given that the total sum collected for admission was $1 200,
(a) calculate the amount each adult paid,
(b) find an equation connecting x and y.

Given further that the number of children attending the concert was $\frac{1}{3}$ of the number of adults, find the total number of people who attended the concert.

35. Two persons, A and B, each has a certain amount of money. If A gives B $3, B will have twice as much as A. If B gives A $7, the amount B has will be one-third that of A. How much does A and B each have?

36. The cost of 4 pencils and 1 ruler is $1. The cost of 7 pencils and 3 rulers is $2.25. Find the cost of 5 pencils and 12 rulers.

37. If the numerator of a fraction is subtracted from 22, the fraction becomes $\frac{1}{3}$. One-fifth of the sum of the numerator and denominator is 8. What is the fraction?

38. There were 200 students at a film show. Some paid $2 each, the rest paid $1 each and the total takings were $320. How many students paid $2 and how many paid $1?

39. A wholesaler sold one type of biscuits at 80¢ per kg and another type at $1.20 per kg. If he had sold them all at $1.00 per kg, he would have received $1.00 less. If he had sold all at $1.20 per kg, he would have received $4.00 more. How many kg of each type of biscuits did he sell?

40. An engineering firm has a machine X which turns out 30 finished products per hour and it has also set up a new machine Y which turns out 40 finished products of the same kind per hour. If 600 of these products were produced on a particular day when the machines were used for a total of 18 hours, how many hours were machines X and Y used?

41. In decimal numerals, a two-digit number is smaller by 54 than the number with the digits reversed. The units digit is three more than twice the tens digit. What is the number?

42. Mrs Chen paid $24 for 2 kg of fresh prawns and 10 kg of tomatoes. Paying the same price for each item, Mrs Lin spent $27 for 1 kg of fresh prawns and 20 kg of tomatoes. What was the price of each kg of fresh prawns and each kg of tomatoes?

43. The figure ABCD shown is a rectangle.
Its measurements are in cm. Calculate
   (a) the length of AB and of BC,
   (b) the perimeter of ABCD,
   (c) the area of ABCD.

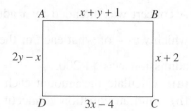

44. A father is three times as old as his son. In 12 years' time, he will be twice as old as his son. How old is the father now?

45. When Mrs Joseph bought five apples and three pears, she reckoned that she would have to pay 80 cents more if she had bought three apples and five pears. What was the difference between the price of one pear and the price of one apple?

46. When Mrs Marcos bought four oranges and a lemon, she paid a total of p cents, but when Mrs Fernando bought four lemons and an orange, she received p cents after giving the fruiterer a five-dollar note. What then was the cost of three oranges and three lemons?

47. The length of a rectangle is 2 cm longer than three times its breadth. If the perimeter of the rectangle is 44 cm, find the length and the breadth of the rectangle.

48. A mother's age is $2\frac{1}{2}$ times the combined ages of her twin daughters. The sum of the ages of the three is 56 years. Find the age of the mother and the age of each twin daughter.

49. $80 is divided between two men such that one-quarter of one person's share is equal to $\frac{1}{6}$ of the other. How much will each man receive?

50. Motorist X and motorist Y start their journey at the same time travelling in the same direction. In 4 hours' time, X will travel 88 km less than Y. If X increases his speed by 12 km/h, his new speed will be $\frac{6}{7}$ of the original travelling speed of Y. Find the travelling speed of each motorist. (Assume that their travelling speeds are constant.)

51. A fraction equals $\frac{1}{2}$ when 5 is added to both the numerator and the denominator. It is equal to 6 when 3 is subtracted from both the numerator and the denominator. Find the numerator and the denominator of the fraction. Hence give the value of the fraction in its simplest form.

52. A man bought a house and a car at a total cost of $640 000. After one year, the value of the house increased by 40% but the value of the car decreased by 20%. Their total value is now $800 000. Calculate the original price of the house and the original price of the car.

53. The figure shown is an equilateral triangle.
    (a) Calculate the length of a side in cm.
    (b) Find the area of the figure if the height is 7.5 cm.

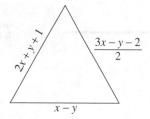

54. The length of a rectangle is greater than its breadth by 2 cm. If the length is increased by 4 cm and the breadth decreased by 3 cm, the area remains the same. Find the length and the breadth of the rectangle.

55. In four years' time, a father will be three times as old as his son. Six years ago, he was seven times as old as his son. How old are they now?

56. Two cars leave town at the same time and travel in opposite directions. The speed of one car is 12 km/h more than the other. They are 444 km apart after three hours. Find the speed of the faster car.

57. Three times Joseph's present age is six years less than his father's present age. Five years ago, the father was seven times as old as his son. How old are they now?

1. The equation of a straight line is given by $x - 2y = 10$.
   (a) Find the gradient and y-intercept of the line. [3]
   (b) Calculate the value of k if the line passes through the point $(k, 3k)$. [2]
   (c) Draw, in the axes provided, the following two straight lines.

       (i) $x = -2$ (ii) $y = \dfrac{3}{2}$ [2]

   Ans (a) _____

         (b) _____

Ans (c)

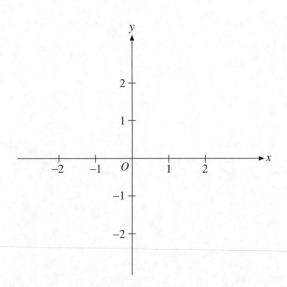

2. Find the point of intersection for each of the following pairs of lines.

(a) $y = 1$
    $y = 4x - 3$

(b) $2x - 3y = 36$
    $4x + 3y = 0$ [5]

Ans (a) _____

     (b) _____

3. Answer the whole of this question on a sheet of graph paper.
A machine can release 36 litres of detergent into a large tank in 5 minutes. In x minutes, the machine can release y litres of detergent.

(a) Write down an equation connecting x and y.   [1]

(b) Copy and complete the table.

x (min)	0	
y (litres)		108

(c) Plot a straight line graph for the table in (b) with the following scales.
                x-axis   4 cm to represent 5 min
                y-axis   1 cm to represent 5 litres   [2]

(d) Use your graph to find approximate answers to the following questions.
    (i) How many minutes does it take the machine to release 16 litres of detergent?

    (ii) How many litres are released into the tank in $9\frac{1}{2}$ minutes?   [2]

Ans (a) _____

     (b) _____

   (d) (i) _____

     (ii) _____

4. Answer the whole of this question on a sheet of graph paper.
The given table of values is for $y = x^2 - 6x + 7$.

x	0	1	2	3	4	5	6
y	7	a	-1	b	-1	2	7

(a) Find a and b. [2]

(b) Using a scale of 2 cm to represent 1 unit on each axis, draw the graph of $y = x^2 - 6x + 7$ for $0 \leqslant x \leqslant 6$. [3]

(c) Use your graph to estimate the value(s) of
   (i) y when $x = 4.5$,
   (ii) x when $y = -0.5$. [2]

(d) What is the minimum value of y? [1]

(e) What is the value of x for which the function $y = x^2 - 6x + 7$ has a minimum? [1]

(f) Where does the curve cut the y-axis? [1]

Ans (a) _____

   (c) (i) _____

   (ii) _____

   (d) _____

   (e) _____

   (f) _____

5. Find the values of x and y in each of the following.

(a) $5xy + y = 24$

$3y + 8 = \dfrac{5}{2}y$ [5]

Ans $x =$ _____

$y =$ _____

(b) $0.3(x - 2y) = \dfrac{1}{4}x - y = 0.5$ [5]

Ans $x =$ _____

$y =$ _____

6.

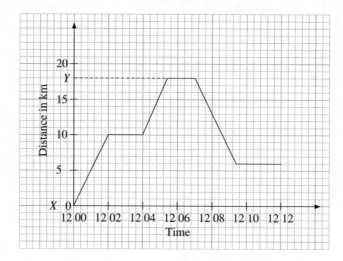

The graph shows the distance-time graph of a particle from X to Y during a period of 12 minutes.

(a) Find the speed of the particle, in km/h, in the first two minutes. [2]

Ans _____

(b) How many times did the particle rest and for how long altogether? [2]

Ans _____

(c) At what speed must the particle travel during the last part of its journey in order to go back to its starting point by 12 15? [2]

Ans _____

(d) Find the distance travelled by the particle between 12 07 and 12 12. [1]

Ans _____

(e) What is the average speed of the particle for the whole journey if it reaches the starting point at 12 15? [2]

Ans _____

(f) A second particle leaves Y for X at 12 02 and travels at a uniform speed of 108 km/h. Draw on the diagram the travel graph of the second particle and hence find the time at which the two particles meet. Give your answer to the nearest second. [3]

Ans _____

CHAPTER 7 / Inequalities

1. Fill in the blanks with '<', '=' or '>'.
   (a) If $m - 2 = n$, then m _____ n.
   (b) 5th _____ 7th
   (c) $a - 3$ _____ $a - 5$
   (d) $10 - k$ _____ $8 - k$
   (e) If $x + 1 = y$, then x _____ $y - 1$.
   (f) If $u > 0$, then $\frac{1}{6}u$ _____ 0.
   (g) If $x > y$, then $\frac{x}{50}$ _____ $\frac{y}{50}$.
   (h) If $x > y$, then $-3x$ _____ $-3y$.
   (i) If $x > y$, then $\frac{1}{x}$ _____ $\frac{1}{y}$.
   (j) If $u > 0$, then $-3u$ _____ 0.

2. Find an inequality in x that represents each of the following solution sets on the number line.

   (a)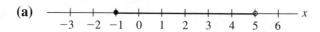

   (b)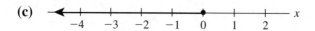

   (c)

   (d)

3. Represent each of the following statements with an inequality. (a, b, c, d and e are real numbers.)
   (a) a is at least 3 but not more than 18.
   (b) b is at least -5 but less than 7.
   (c) c is more than $\frac{1}{2}$.
   (d) d is not less than $2\frac{1}{3}$.
   (e) e is at most -3.

64

4. Represent the set of values of x on a number line such that
$$3x + 7 > 5x - 4,$$
and x represents
(a) real numbers,
(b) positive integers,
(c) non-negative real numbers,
(d) positive real numbers,
(e) non-negative integers,
(f) prime numbers,
(g) odd numbers.

5. Solve each of the following inequalities and then draw the solution set on a number line. (x is a real number unless otherwise stated.)
(a) $3 < 2x + 15$ and $-8 \leqslant x \leqslant -3$ where x is an integer.
(b) $7x < 65$ and $25 - 2x \leqslant 12$ where x is an integer.
(c) $4x - 7 \leqslant -5$
(d) $7 - \frac{3}{2}x \geqslant 16$
(e) $3(x - 1) > 7 - 2x$
(f) $2(x - 5) + 18 < 3(2x + 1)$
(g) $\frac{1}{3}(2x - 1) > \frac{3}{5}x$
(h) $\frac{1}{4}(x + 4) \leqslant \frac{1}{3}(x + 1)$
(i) $\frac{x}{10} \leqslant \frac{1}{6}(2 - x) - 3$
(j) $\frac{1}{2}(3x + 2) \geqslant \frac{1}{3}(7 - 2x)$

6. Solve the following inequalities.
(a) $2x - 3 < 5 - 4x$
(b) $3\left(x + \frac{1}{3}\right) \geqslant \frac{1}{2}(x - 4)$
(c) $7x - 4(x + 5) \leqslant 13(2 - x)$
(d) $\frac{x + 3}{4} > \frac{2x - 3}{5}$
(e) $6 + \frac{2x + 1}{3} < x$
(f) $\frac{3x - 2}{3} - \frac{2x - 3}{6} > 0$
(g) $2x + 1 \geqslant \frac{x}{3}$
(h) $\frac{3x}{5} - \frac{1}{2} \leqslant \frac{1}{4} - 2x$
(i) $\frac{x}{3} + \frac{x - 3}{4} - \frac{2x - 7}{2} > 0$
(j) $\frac{3x - 4}{5} - \frac{x + 1}{4} \leqslant \frac{2}{3}$

7. Given that $-3 < x \leqslant 7\frac{1}{3}$, write down
(a) the largest integer value of x,
(b) the smallest integer value of x,
(c) the largest rational value of x,
(d) the difference between the smallest and the largest prime number.

8. Given that $35 - 4x \leqslant 13$, find
   (a) the least value of x,
   (b) the least integer value of x.

9. Find the greatest prime number x such that $2x + 1 \leqslant 25$.

10. Given that $2 \leqslant a \leqslant 5$ and $-7 \leqslant b \leqslant 3$, find
    (a) the greatest possible value of $a + b$,
    (b) the greatest possible value of $a - b$,
    (c) the least possible value of ab,
    (d) the least possible value of $\dfrac{a}{b}$,
    (e) the least possible value of $a^2 + b^2$,
    (f) the greatest possible value of $a^2 + b^2$.

11. Solve the following inequalities. Represent the solution set on a number line.

    (a) $3x - 5 \leqslant 2(x + 1) - (9 - 2x)$
    (b) $\dfrac{8 - x}{3} > \dfrac{2x + 3}{5}$

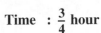

MID-TERM ASSESSMENT PAPER 1

Time : $\frac{3}{4}$ hour

Marks : **40**

ALL questions may be attempted.

Answers are to be written on the question paper in the spaces provided.

Omission of essential workings will result in loss of marks. No calculators are allowed.

This paper consists of 15 questions.

1. Evaluate the following.

    (a) $\dfrac{3^0 \times 3}{3^{-3}}$ [2]

    (b) $\left(\dfrac{5}{4}\right)^{-2}$ [1]

    Ans (a) _____

    (b) _____

2. Express the following in standard form.

    (a) 0.002 04 [1]

    (b) 14.1×10^3 [1]

    Ans (a) _____

    (b) _____

67

3. Simplify $(2a^2 \times a^{-3})^6$. [2]

Ans _____

4. Simplify $\dfrac{\frac{5a^2}{3}}{\frac{10}{9a}}$. [2]

Ans _____

5. Solve the following inequality. [3]
$$3 < 5 + 4x$$

Ans _____

6. Factorise the following completely.
   (a) $12x - 27x^2$ [1]
   (b) $2p + 6 - pq - 3q$ [2]

Ans (a) _____

(b) _____

7. Find, by factorisation, the value of $3.61^2 - 1.39^2$. [3]

Ans _____

8. Solve the equation $\dfrac{4}{2(3-x)} = 5$. [3]

Ans _____

9. Express $\dfrac{1+a}{a^2} - \dfrac{1}{a}$ as a fraction in its simplest form. [3]

Ans _____

10. In a sale, all prices are reduced by 20%. Calculate the original price of an article whose selling price is $35.20. [2]

Ans _____

11. The equations of two straight lines are $y = 2x - 1$ and $y = 6x - 4$. Calculate the coordinates of the point of intersection of these two lines. [3]

Ans _____

12. Find the solution to the equation $2(3y^2 - 1) = y$. [3]

Ans _____

13. A rectangular field has sides $5x$ metres and $3x$ metres. Calculate the value of x if the cost of buying the field at $4 per m^2 is $4 860. [3]

Ans _____

14. On the axes provided, sketch the graph of
   (a) $x = -2$,
   (b) $x + 2y = 4$. [2]

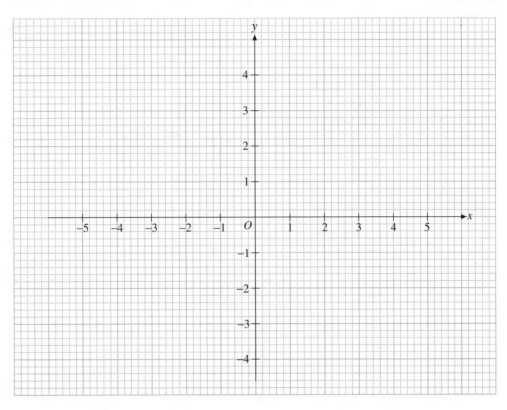

15. On a certain day, Mabel spent 3 h 20 min of her time on housework, watching television programmes and reading the newspapers, in the ratio $5 : 11 : 4$ respectively. How many minutes did she spend washing clothes if this task took up 18% of the time spent on housework? [3]

Ans _____

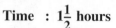

MID-TERM ASSESSMENT PAPER 2

Time : $1\frac{1}{2}$ **hours**

Marks : 60

This paper consists of 2 sections.
Section A consists of **6 questions.**
Section B consists of **5 questions**.
Calculators may be used in this paper. If the degree of accuracy is not specified and if the answer is not exact, the answer should be given to three significant figures.

Section A (28 marks)
ALL *questions may be attempted.*

1. **(a)**   Simplify $\dfrac{(p^{-2}q^4)^3}{pq^{-5}}$. [2]

Ans _____

   (b)   Find the value of $\dfrac{p}{3q}$ when $p = 1.2 \times 10^{-6}$ and $q = 4.32 \times 10^{-4}$. Express your answers in the standard form, correct to three significant figures. [2]

Ans _____

2. Express the following as a single fraction in its simplest form.

$$\frac{3}{2x - 3} - \frac{2}{6 - 4x}$$ [4]

Ans _____

3. **(a)** Given $x = \dfrac{AL}{A + L}$, express A in terms of x and L.

(b) Hence, or otherwise, find the value of A if $x = -2$ and $L = 2$. [4]

Ans (a) _____

(b) _____

4. Expand and simplify the following.
   (a) $3(3m - 2)(m + 1)$ [2]
   (b) $(a + 4)^2 - (a - 4)^2$ [3]

   Ans (a) _____

   (b) _____

5. An express train left station X at 07 45 and arrived at station Y at 11 15. If it travelled at a constant speed of 54 km/h, what was the distance travelled? If it increased its speed by 9 km/h, at what time would it arrive at station Y? [5]

   Ans _____

6. The diagram shows the travel graphs for a car and a bicycle between two towns A and B which is 35 km apart.

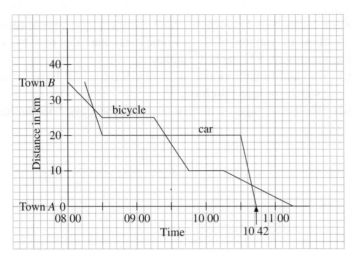

(a) Where do the car and the bicycle begin their journey? [1]

Ans _____

(b) What is the average speed of the car for the whole journey? [2]

Ans _____

(c) When does the bicycle stop to rest and for how long altogether? [2]

Ans _____

(d) Find the greatest speed of the bicycle during its journey. [1]

Ans _____

Section B (32 marks)
Answer any **FOUR** *questions.*

1. **(a)** Ramee can buy a watch for $550 if she pays cash immediately or on hire purchase by paying 60% downpayment and the rest by 12 equal monthly instalments of $22 each. Calculate
   (i) the additional amount of money Ramee will have to pay if she buys the watch on hire purchase,
   (ii) the percentage of money saved if she pays $550 immediately.   [4]

Ans (i) _____

(ii) _____

(b) By selling the watch for $550, the shopkeeper makes a profit of $110. What is the shopkeeper's percentage profit?   [2]

Ans _____

(c) Due to inflation, the cash price of the watch is increased by 15%. What is the new selling price of the watch? [2]

Ans _____

2. (a) Solve the inequality $\frac{2}{3}(4x - 3) < -\frac{1}{6}(x - 5)$. [4]

Ans _____

(b) Jeremy bought 12 dozen pens for $28 and he sold each of them for 35 cents. What is the least number of these pens he must sell in order to make a profit of at least 30%? [4]

Ans _____

3. A dealer bought 9 toys at $\$x$ per toy. He proposed to sell each toy at a profit of $3 per toy.

(a) Write down an expression, in terms of x, for the selling price of each toy. [1]

Ans _____

(b) He found that he was only able to sell x toys at this price. Write down an expression, in terms of x, for the total amount of money he received from selling these x toys. [1]

Ans _____

(c) Given that the dealer received $88 altogether, form an equation in x and show that it reduces to $x^2 + 3x - 88 = 0$. [2]

Ans _____

(d) Solve this equation for x and hence write down the dealer's profit. [4]

$$Ans \quad x = \underline{\hspace{4cm}}$$

$$Profit = \underline{\hspace{4cm}}$$

4. Simplify the following, giving your answers in the lowest terms.

(a) $\dfrac{3uv - 2v - 12u + 8}{8 - 10u - 3u^2}$ [2]

$$Ans \underline{\hspace{5cm}}$$

(b) $\dfrac{6x^2 + 7x - 5}{9x^2 - 25} \div \dfrac{2x^3 - x^2}{3x}$ [2]

$$Ans \underline{\hspace{5cm}}$$

(c) $\dfrac{2k^2 - k - 3}{12k} \div \dfrac{4k^2 - 9}{6k^2 + 9k}$ [2]

Ans _____

(d) $\dfrac{6 - 3y}{3y^2 - 12} \times \dfrac{(y + 2)(2 - y)}{y - 2}$ [2]

Ans _____

5. **Answer the whole of this question on a sheet of graph paper.**

The variables x and y are connected by the equation $y = x^2 - x - 2$.
(a) Complete the table below for some corresponding values of x and y.

x	-3	-2	-1	0	1	2	3	4	5
y	10	4		-2	-2	0		10	18

[2]

(b) Taking 2 cm to represent 1 unit on both axes, draw the graph of $y = x^2 - x - 2$ for values of x in the range $-3 \leqslant x \leqslant 5$. [3]

(c) Use your graph to find
    (i) the values of x when $y = 2.3$,
    (ii) the minimum value of $x^2 - x - 2$,
    (iii) the equation of the line of symmetry. [3]

CHAPTER 8

Congruent and Similar Triangles

1. Study each of the following figures (not drawn to scale) and show that there is a pair of congruent triangles. Write a correct statement of congruence and state the test used.

(a)
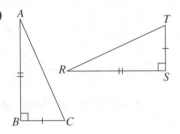

(b)
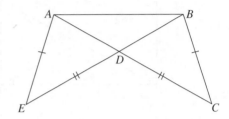

(c)
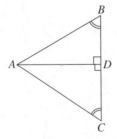

(d)
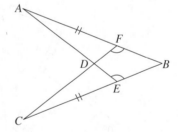

(e)
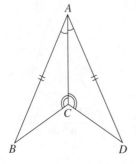

(f)
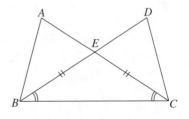

(g)

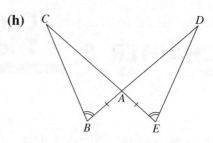

(h)

(i)

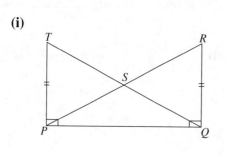

(j)

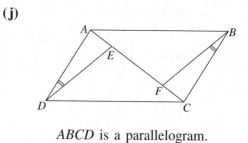

ABCD is a parallelogram.

2. Find *x* and *y* if the triangles are congruent.

(a)

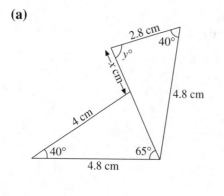

(b)

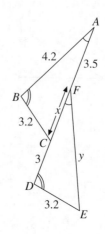

(c)

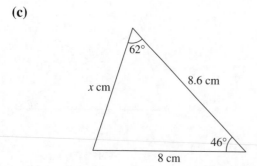

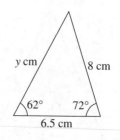

(d)

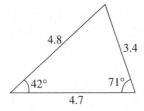

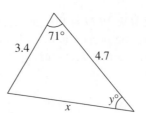

(e)

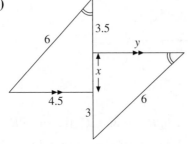

(f)

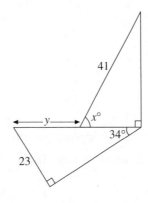

3.

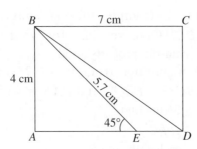

In the figure, *ABCD* is a rectangle.

(a) Name the triangle that is congruent to triangle *XYZ*. State the case of congruency.

(b) Find the area of triangle *XYZ*.

4.

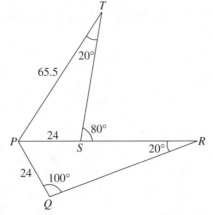

(a) Prove that △*PQR* is congruent to △*PST*.

(b) Find the length of *RS*.

(c) Find *TP̂S*.

5. In △*LMN*, $N\hat{L}M = 90°$ and *LM* = *LN*. *AB* is any straight line through *L* and *MY* and *NX* are the perpendiculars from *M* and *N* to *AB* respectively. Complete the diagram and prove that *LX* = *MY*.

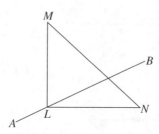

6. *A* is the midpoint of the side *QR* of △*PQR*. *B* and *C* lie on *PR* and *PQ* respectively so that $A\hat{B}R = A\hat{C}Q = 90°$ and *AB* = *AC*. Prove that *PQ* = *PR*.

7.

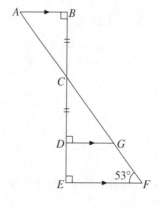

(a) Name a triangle that is congruent to △*ABC*. Give reasons for your answer and state the property used.

(b) Given another triangle *PQR* such that △*ABC* ≡ △*PRQ* and *AB* = 4 cm and *BC* = 3 cm, find

    (i) $Q\hat{P}R$,

    (ii) the length of *PR*,

    (iii) area of △*PQR*.

For questions 8 to 21, find the sides marked with letters. All lengths are given in centimetres. (Diagrams are not drawn to scale.)

8.

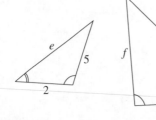

9.

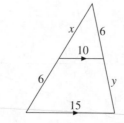

84

10.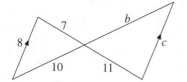

11.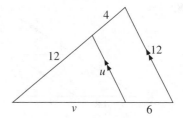

12.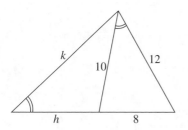

13.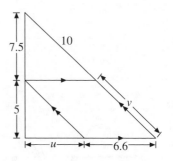

14.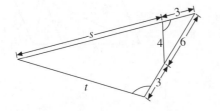

15.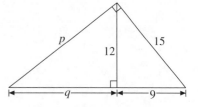

16.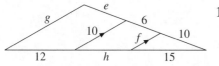

17.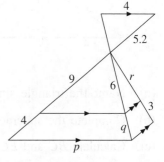

18.

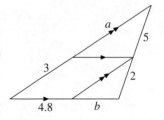

19.

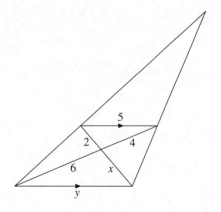

20.

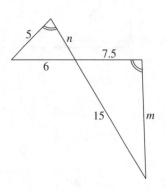

21.

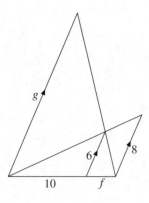

22.

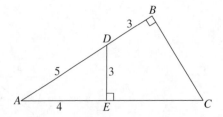

(a) Name the triangle similar to $\triangle ABC$.

(b) Complete the statement: $\dfrac{AB}{(\quad)} = \dfrac{(\quad)}{AD} = \dfrac{BC}{ED}$.

(c) Calculate BC and EC.

23.

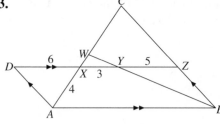

In the diagram, $BC /\!/ AD$, $DZ /\!/ AB$, $DX = 6$ cm, $XY = 3$ cm, $YZ = 5$ cm and $AX = 4$ cm.

(a) **(i)** Name a triangle similar to $\triangle XDA$.

     (ii) Calculate CX.

(b) **(i)** Name a triangle similar to $\triangle WXY$.

     (ii) Calculate WX.

24.

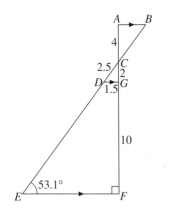

In the diagram, $AC = 4$ cm, $CD = 2.5$ cm, $DG = 1.5$ cm, $CG = 2$ cm, $GF = 10$ cm and $D\hat{E}F = 53.1°$.

(a) Name two triangles which are similar.

(b) Calculate AB, DE and EF.

(c) Given that $\triangle PQR \equiv \triangle CAB$, write down

    (i) the length of PQ,

    (ii) the size of $Q\hat{P}R$.

25.

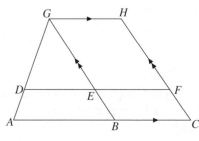

(a) If $AD = 3$ cm, $AG = 9$ cm and $CH = 12$ cm, find GE.

(b) If $AD = 1$ cm, $DG = 2$ cm and $GE = 4$ cm, find HC.

26. The length of the sides of a hexagon are 9 cm, 11.7 cm, 15 cm, 4.8 cm, 19.2 cm and 12.3 cm respectively. If the shortest side of a similar hexagon is 1.6 cm, find the lengths of its other sides. Find also its perimeter.

27. A tree casts a shadow 10 m long while a 2 m pole casts a shadow 3 m long. How tall is the tree?

28. A line from the top of a cliff to the ground just passes over the top of a telephone pole 6 m high. The line meets the ground at a point 4.5 m from the base of the pole. If the line is 36 m from this point to the base of the cliff, how high is the cliff?

29. Three vertical sticks are shown in the diagram. The ends of the sticks A, B and C are in a straight line. What is the length of the tallest stick?

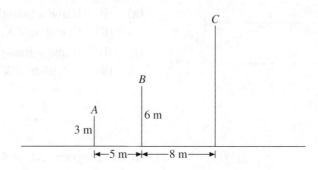

30.

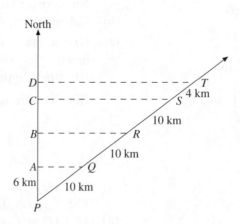

A hiker walks in a straight line from P to T and stops every 10 km for a rest at Q, R and S. At Q, he is 6 km further North than he was at P.

How much further North than P is he at

(a) R,

(b) S,

(c) T?

1.

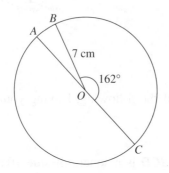

Calculate
(a) the length of arc *BC*,
(b) the area of sector *AOB*.

$$\left(\text{Take } \pi = \frac{22}{7}\right)$$

2. (a) The length of the minor arc *XY* is $\frac{5}{12}$ of the circumference of the circle, calculate the minor angle *XOY*.

(b) Given that the length of the minor arc *XY* is 110 cm, calculate the radius of the circle.

$$\left(\text{Take } \pi = \frac{22}{7}\right)$$

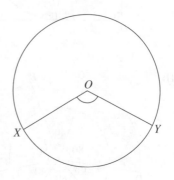

3.

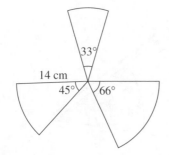

The figure is made up of three unequal sectors each of radius 14 cm. The angles subtended at the centre are 33°, 45° and 66° respectively. Using $\pi = \frac{22}{7}$, find the area and perimeter of the figure.

4. In the figure, $OP = 24$ cm, $OQ = 39$ cm and $S\hat{O}P = 140°$.

Taking π to be $\frac{22}{7}$, find

(a) the shaded area,

(b) the perimeter of *PQRS*,

(c) the ratio $\dfrac{\text{arc length } QR}{\text{arc length } PS}$.

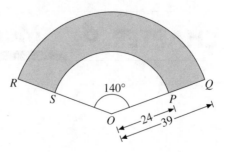

5. Find the area of the shaded portion in each of the following, leaving your answer in terms of π.

(a)

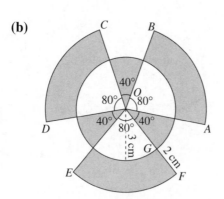

ABCD is a square of side 10 cm.

(b)

(c)

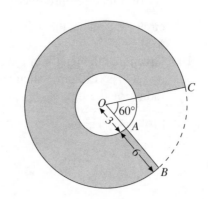

6. Find the ratio of area *A* to area *B*.

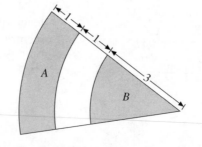

7.

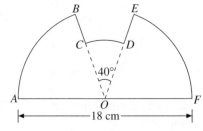

The figure is made up of a sector OCD and two equal sectors OAB and OEF; $C\hat{O}D = 40°$ and $AF = 18$ cm. Using $\pi = \frac{22}{7}$,

(a) write down the size of $A\hat{O}B$,

(b) find the length of arc AB,

(c) if arc $CD = 4.4$ cm, find the radius of the sector OCD,

(d) find the perimeter of the figure $OABCDEF$.

8.

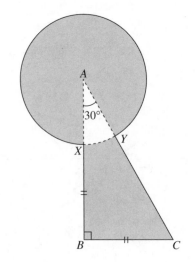

In the figure, $BX = BC = 3$ cm, $X\hat{A}Y = 30°$ and $AY = 2.2$ cm.

Using $\pi = 3.14$, find

(a) the area of the circle, giving your answer to four significant figures,

(b) the area of the triangle ABC,

(c) the area of the minor sector AXY, giving your answer to two decimal places,

(d) the shaded area, giving your answer to the nearest whole number.

9.

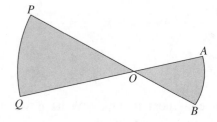

In the diagram, $OP = 20$ cm, $OA = \frac{1}{2}OP$ and arc $PQ = 6.28$ cm.

Using $\pi = 3.14$, find

(a) $P\hat{O}Q$,

(b) area of the figure.

10. A piece of wire 3.72 m long is used to make sectors as shown. How many sectors can be made from the given piece of wire?

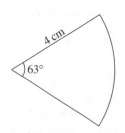

11. A piece of string 70.5 cm long goes exactly once round the edge of a plate in the form of a sector as shown. Calculate the area of the sector.

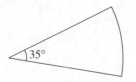

12.

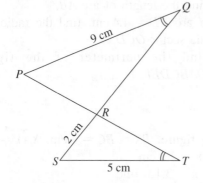

(a) Name a triangle similar to $\triangle PQR$.

(b) Find PR.

(c) Express as a fraction, the ratio

$$\frac{\text{area of } \triangle PQR}{\text{area of } \triangle STR}.$$

13. (a) Name the triangles that are similar.

(b) What is the ratio of $\dfrac{QR}{RS}$?

(c) Calculate x.

(d) If area of $\triangle PQR = 30 \text{ cm}^2$, find the area of $\triangle TSR$.

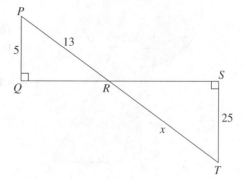

14.

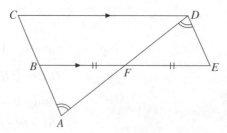

(a) Study the figure. Find a pair of congruent triangles. Write down a correct statement of congruency and state the property used.

(b) Name a triangle similar to $\triangle ABF$.

(c) Find the ratio of

(i) $\dfrac{AF}{FD}$,

(ii) $\dfrac{BF}{CD}$.

(d) If $CD = 8$ cm, find FE.

(e) Given that the area of $\triangle ABF$ is 12 cm^2, find the area of $\triangle ACD$.

(f) Hence write down the area of the quadrilateral $BCDE$.

15.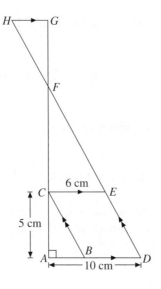

Given that $HG \parallel CE \parallel AD$, $CB \parallel ED$, $CA = 5$ cm, $CE = 6$ cm, $AD = 10$ cm and $G\hat{A}D = 90°$, calculate

(a) the area of the parallelogram $BDEC$,

(b) the length of FC,

(c) the area of $\triangle FGH$ if $FC : FG = 3 : 1$.

16.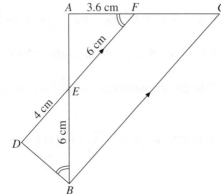

(a) Show that the triangles AEF and BED are congruent. Write a correct statement of congruence and state the case of congruence.

(b) Find

   (i) FC,

   (ii) BC,

   (iii) area of $\triangle ABC$ if area of $\triangle AEF$ is 7 cm^2.

(c) What is the area of the trapezium $DBCF$?

17. A statue stands on a base of area 504 cm^2 and a model of it has a base of area 14 cm^2. Find the weight of the statue if the model weighs 5 kg.

18. Three cups A, B and C are 4 cm, 6 cm and 2 cm high respectively. If cup B has a volume of 54 cm^3 and a surface area of 21 cm^2, find

(a) the volume of cup A,

(b) the surface area of cup C.

19. A pentagon has sides 4 cm, 5 cm, 6 cm, x cm and 8 cm respectively. A similar pentagon has the corresponding shortest side 12 cm. Find

(a) the longest side of the larger pentagon,

(b) the value of x if the perimeter of the larger pentagon is 90 cm,

(c) the ratio of the area of the smaller pentagon to that of the larger pentagon.

93

20. The volumes of two metal jugs are 24 cm^3 and 3 000 cm^3 respectively. If the smaller jug has a surface area of 11 cm^2, find
   (a) the ratio of the heights of the jugs,
   (b) the mass of the smaller jug if the bigger jug weighs 62.5 kg, giving your answer in grams,
   (c) the surface area of the bigger jug,
   (d) the density, in g/cm^3, of the metal used in making the jugs.

21. The areas of the bases of two toy ships are in the ratio 9 : 16.
   (a) Find the ratio of the heights of the ships.
   (b) If the mass of the smaller ship is 108 g, what is the mass of the larger ship?
   (c) The density of the material which the ships are made of is 0.9 g/cm^3. Find the volumes of the two ships.

22. Two scale models, A and B, of a castle are made. The length of model B is $\frac{4}{5}$ of the length of model A.
   (a) Given that the height of the tower in model A is 75 cm, what is the height of the tower in model B?
   (b) If the area of the windows in model B is 3 200 cm^2, what is the area of the windows in model A?
   (c) What is the ratio of the volumes of air in the dining rooms of the two models?

23. The areas of two spheres are 108 cm^2 and 48 cm^2 respectively. Find the ratio of
   (a) their radii,
   (b) their volumes,
   (c) their masses.

24. The ratio of the volumes of two similar solid cylinders is 27 : 125. If the bigger cylinder has a height of 25 cm, a base area of 1 020 cm^2 and a mass of 30 g, find the height, base area and mass of the smaller cylinder.

25. The surface area of one sphere is $2\frac{1}{4}$ times the surface area of another. Given that the radius of the smaller sphere is 6 cm, calculate the radius of the larger sphere.

26. A beaker of height 10 cm holds 500 cm^3 of liquid. Find the height of a similar beaker which holds 4 litres of liquid.

27. The surface areas of two jugs A and B are 160 cm^2 and 250 cm^2 respectively.
   (a) What is the ratio of their heights?
   (b) If jug B can hold 2 150 cm^3 of water, how much water can jug A hold?

28. The sides of a triangle *ABC* are *x* cm, 9 cm and 6 cm respectively. If the perimeter of a similar triangle *PQR* is 14 cm and the ratio of their areas is 9 : 4, find
    (a) the ratio of their corresponding sides,
    (b) an expression for the ratio of the perimeter, in terms of *x*. Hence form an equation in terms of *x* and solve for *x*,
    (c) the lengths of the sides that make up △*PQR*.

29. The lengths of two similar toy planes are 4 cm and 10 cm respectively.
    (a) Find the ratio of the surface areas of the bigger toy plane to the smaller toy plane.
    (b) If the bigger toy plane has a capacity of 62.5 cm^3, find the volume of the smaller toy plane.

30. Two vases are geometrically similar and one is $2\frac{1}{2}$ times as long as the other.
    (a) Given that the height of the smaller vase is 14 cm, calculate the height of the larger vase.
    (b) Write down the ratio of the surface area of the smaller vase to the larger vase.
    (c) If the capacity of the larger vase is 250 cm^3, find the capacity of the smaller vase.

31. Find the unknown length, *l*, unknown area, *S*, and unknown volume, *V*, in each of the following pairs of similar objects.
    (a)

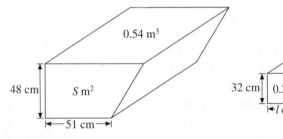

    (b)

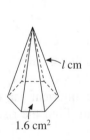
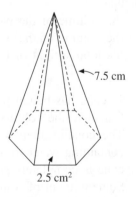

$$\text{Volume} = 2.4 \text{ cm}^3$$
$$\text{Total surface area} = 4 \text{ cm}^2$$

$$\text{Volume} = V \text{ cm}^3$$
$$\text{Total surface area} = S \text{ cm}^2$$

32. The volumes of two spheres are 640 cm^3 and 270 cm^3. Find the ratios of
    (a) their diameters,
    (b) their surface areas,
    (c) their masses.

33. The masses of two similar marble toys are 8.58 kg and 4.29 kg. The first toy is 12.94 cm high and has a surface area of 54 cm^2. What is the height and surface area of the second toy?

34. A statue has a base of area 7.04 m^2. A similar model has a base of area 800 cm^2. Find, in tonnes, the mass of the statue if the model weighs 40 kg.

35. A toy house is an exact model of a real one. The volumes of air in the kitchens are 27 500 cm^3 and 220 m^3 respectively. The area of the front door of the real house is 7 m^2. Find the area of the front door of the doll's house.

36. Two similar objects have surface areas A_1 and A_2, such that $9A_1 = 16A_2$. If their volumes are V_1 and V_2 respectively and are such that $V_1 = kV_2$, write down the value of k.

37. The figure shows the vertical section of a solid paper weight made in the shape of a circular cone. Its height is 9 cm and the diameter of its base is 7 cm. The shaded portion is 3 cm thick and is made of lead, while the unshaded portion is made of wood. Lead weighs 13.6 g/cm^3 and wood weighs 0.9 g/cm^3.
    Calculate
    (a) the volume of the paper weight,
    (b) the volume of the wooden portion,
    (c) the total weight of the paper weight.

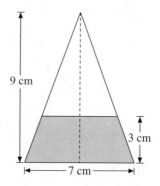

38. A solid cone has height 9 cm and base radius 4 cm.
    (a) Calculate the volume of the cone.
    (b) The cone is then lowered into a cylindrical jar of base radius 8 cm and containing water to a height of 15 cm. Find the rise in water level when the cone is completely submerged.
    (c) Some amount of water is poured away so that the height of water left in the cylinder is 10 cm, while the cone remained submerged. Calculate the percentage of water being poured away, giving your answer to three significant figures.

39. (a) A solid cylinder of radius 7 cm and height 8 cm has a density of 5 g/cm^3. Find
    (i) the volume of the cylinder,
    (ii) the mass of the cylinder in kilograms.

(b) The cylinder is melted down and a certain amount of the molten liquid is used to cast into a sphere of radius 6.5 cm. The unused liquid is thrown away.
    (i) What is the volume of the sphere?
    (ii) What percentage of the molten liquid is thrown away?

40. A square metal plate of side 30 cm has four equal holes each of radius 5 cm drilled in it.

(a) Calculate the surface area of the metal plate, using $\pi = 3.14$.

(b) If the thickness of the plate is 6 mm, calculate the volume of the plate.

(c) Given that the density of the metal used in making the plate is 2.5 g/cm^3, find the cost by weight of the metal plate if each gram of the metal is sold at 20 cents.

41. (a) The diagram shows a right pyramid with a horizontal rectangular base *ABCD* and vertex *V*. The volume of the pyramid is 324 cm^3 and the area of the base is 216 cm^2. Calculate the height *VX* of the pyramid.

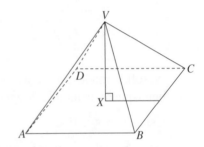

(b) The diagram shows a container which is made by fixing a hollow hemisphere of internal radius 44 cm to one rim of a hollow right cylinder of the same internal radius and of height *h* cm. The hemispherical part of the container is completely filled with water.
    (i) Calculate the volume of the water in litres.
    (ii) Given that a further 50 *l* of water is needed to fill the container completely, calculate the height, *h* cm, of the cylinder.

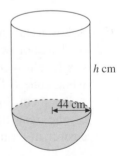

(Take $\pi = 3.14$, giving your answers to two decimal places.)

42. Seven solid spheres are melted down to form a pyramid with the base of a pentagon. If the radius of each sphere is 3 cm and the height of the pyramid is 33 cm, find

(a) the volume of the seven spheres,

(b) the area of the pentagon.

$\left(\text{Take } \pi = \dfrac{22}{7}\right)$

43.

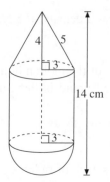

Find, in terms of π, the volume and the total surface area of the solid, which is made by joining a cone, of base radius 3 cm, height 4 cm and slant height 5 cm, to a cylinder and a hemisphere, as shown in the diagram. The height of the solid is 14 cm.

44.

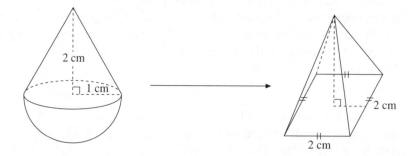

A solid, made up of a cone (height 2 cm and base radius 1 cm) joined to a hemisphere, is melted down to form a pyramid with a square base of side 2 cm long.

Using $\pi = \dfrac{22}{7}$, find

(a) the volume of the solid,

(b) the height of the pyramid.

45. A boy used super-glue to stick together the bases of two cones A and B. Cone A has height 4 cm and base radius 3 cm, while cone B has height 3 cm and base radius 4 cm. Find the total surface area of the resulting solid, leaving your answer in terms of π.

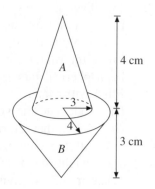

46. A hemisphere of radius 7 cm is placed on top of a rectangular block 20 cm by 15 cm by 10 cm. Find, giving your answers to two decimal places,

(a) the area of the uncovered top of the block,

(b) the volume of the resulting solid,

(c) the mass of the solid, in kg, if 1 cm^3 weighs 20 g.

$\left(\text{Take } \pi = \dfrac{22}{7}\right)$

47. The internal dimensions of a rectangular wooden box are 22 cm by 16 cm by 6 cm.
   (a) When the lid is closed, calculate
      (i) the internal volume of the box,
      (ii) the number of cubes of side 2 cm which will completely fill the box,
      (iii) the maximum number of cubes of side 3 cm which can be fitted inside the box.
   (b) The external dimensions of the closed wooden box are 24 cm by 18 cm by 8 cm. Calculate the volume of wood used in making the box.
   (c) If the mass of the empty box is 1.2 kg, find the density of wood, giving your answer in grams per cubic centimetre, correct to three significant figures.

48.

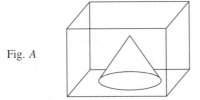
Fig. A

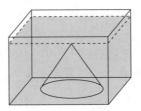
Fig. B

An open rectangular tank of depth 55 cm has a horizontal base of length 60 cm and breadth 50 cm. A solid metal cone of volume 12 000 cm^3 rests with its base on the base of the tank as shown in Fig. A. 72 000 cm^3 of water is poured into the tank at a rate of 108 cm^3/s.
   (a) How many minutes does it take for all the water to be poured in?
   (b) Given that the water just covers the vertex of the cone as shown in Fig. B, calculate
      (i) the depth of the water,
      (ii) the radius of the cone. (Take π to be 3.142)
   (c) The cone is now removed from the tank. Calculate by how much the water level falls.

49. A bowl is made by cutting into half a hollow sphere of external diameter 54 cm, made of metal 1.5 cm thick. If the bowl is filled with a liquid of density 32.15 kg/m^3, calculate the total mass of liquid in the bowl. The bowl when empty weighs 91.8 kg. Calculate the density, in kg/m^3, of the metal of which the bowl is made.

50. A cylinder of height 20 cm and diameter 12 cm is one-third full of water. If six circular discs of diameter 3.6 cm and thickness 2.8 mm are dropped into the cylinder and totally submerged, find the rise in water level.

51. The arc of a sector of a circle, of radius 15 cm, is 54 cm long. If the sector is folded to form the curved surface area of a cone without overlapping, find
   (a) the base radius of the cone,
   (b) the curved surface area of the cone.

52. Two solid spheres have surface areas $100\pi \text{ cm}^2$ and $196\pi \text{ cm}^2$ respectively. They are melted and recast to form a larger sphere. Find the approximate surface area of the larger sphere in cm^2.

53. A solid cone of height 4 cm and radius 3 cm is cut into two along a vertical axis of symmetry. Calculate the total surface area of the two resultant solids. $\left(\text{Take } \pi = \frac{22}{7}\right)$

54. A given right pyramid with a square base of side x cm and height h cm has a volume of 3.6 cm^3. If x becomes $15x$ and h becomes $\frac{1}{3}h$, find the new volume in cm^3.

55. Calculate the slant height of a cone if its total surface area is $\frac{2\,200}{7} \text{ cm}^2$ and its radius is 5 cm.

56. Find the total surface area of a hemisphere if its volume is $144\pi \text{ cm}^3$.

57. Find the volume of the resulting solid when a pyramid 4 cm high is removed from a pyramid 10 cm high with a square base of side 15 cm.

58. A right circular cone with base of diameter 10 cm is cut by a plane parallel to the base. The height of the frustum (shaded part) is 6 cm and the radius of the small cone cut off is 2 cm. Find
  (a) the height of the right circular cone,
  (b) the volume of the frustum (shaded part) and leave your answer correct to two decimal places. (Take $\pi = 3.142$)

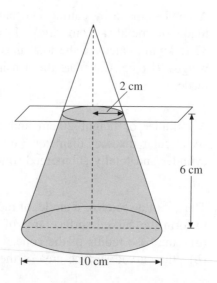

59. A test tube consists of a cylinder and a hemisphere of the same radius. 282 cm³ of water are required to fill the whole tube and 262 cm³ are required to fill it to a level which is 1 cm below the top of the tube. Taking $\pi = 3.142$, calculate, giving your answers correct to three significant figures,

(a) the radius of the tube,

(b) the length of the cylindrical part of the tube.

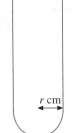

60.

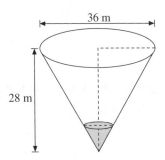

The diagram shows a container in the form of a cone, whose vertex is downwards and whose axis is vertical. The diameter of the circular top is 36 m and the height of the cone is 28 m. The cone is filled with water to a depth of one-quarter of the height of the cone.

(a) Calculate

    (i) the radius of the horizontal surface of the water,

    (ii) the volume of the water in the cone.

$$\left(\text{Take } \pi = \frac{22}{7}\right)$$

(b) Water is added into the container through a pipe of cross-sectional area 0.5 m² at a constant rate of 10 m/s. Calculate the time taken to fill the container completely. Give your answer in minutes and seconds.

61. The area of the bases of two similar wooden paper weights are in the ratio 9 : 16.

(a) Find the ratio of their heights.

(b) State the ratio of their surface areas.

(c) If the volume of the smaller paper weight is 810 cm³, find

    (i) the volume of the larger paper weight,

    (ii) the mass of the smaller paper weight if the density of wood is 0.9 g/cm³.

1.

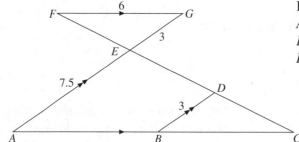

In the diagram, *FG // AC*, *AG // BD*, *FG* = 6 cm, *EG* = 3 cm, *AE* = 7.5 cm and *BD* = 3 cm.

(a) Show that the triangles *BCD* and *EFG* are congruent. Write a correct statement of congruence and state the case of congruency. [3]

Ans _____

(b) Find the length of *AC*. [3]

Ans _____

(c) Find the ratio *CD* : *DE*. [3]

Ans _____

(d) Given that area of $\triangle EFG = 2.8 \text{ cm}^2$, find the area of quadrilateral *ABDE*.

[4]

Ans _____

2.

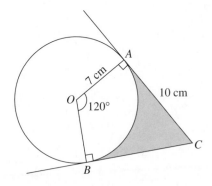

Given that *O* is the centre of the circle and two tangents from point *C* touch the circle at points *A* and *B*. The radius of the circle is 7 cm, angle $AOB = 120°$ and $AC = BC = 10$ cm.

Find, giving your answer as a fraction in its simplest form,

(a) the area of the minor sector *OAB*, [3]

(b) the area and perimeter of the shaded portion. [6]

$\left(\text{Take } \pi = \dfrac{22}{7}\right)$

Ans (a) _____

(b) _____

3.

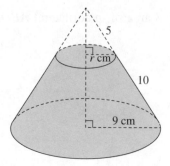

The diagram shows a frustum, which is obtained by removing the cone of base radius r cm from the cone of base radius 9 cm.

(a) Calculate the value of r. [2]

Ans _____

(b) Find, in terms of π, the
    (i) curved surface area of the cone removed, [2]
    (ii) curved surface area of the original cone, [2]
    (iii) total surface area of the frustum. [4]

Ans (i) _____

    (ii) _____

    (iii) _____

4. The heights of two similar vases are in the ratio $5 : 4$.
   (a) State the ratio of the circumference of their bases. [1]

   Ans _____

   (b) If the surface area of the larger vase is 12.5 m^2, what is the surface area of the smaller vase? [3]

   Ans _____

   (c) If the mass of the smaller vase is 6.4 kg, what is the mass of the larger vase? [3]

   Ans _____

   (d) Given that the density of the material in which the vases are made from is 12.8 g/cm^3, find the volume of the material used in making the smaller vase. [3]

   Ans _____

5.

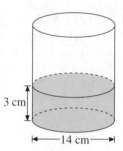 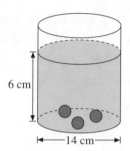

A cylindrical can with diameter 14 cm contains water up to a height of 3 cm. When three equal spheres are placed in it, the water level rises to a height of 6 cm. Using $\pi = \frac{22}{7}$, find

(a) the volume of water displaced, [2]

Ans _____

(b) the volume of one sphere, [2]

Ans _____

(c) the radius of one sphere, giving your answer correct to three significant figures.

[4]

Ans _____

1.

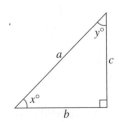

Express c in terms of
(a) a and b,
(b) a and x,
(c) a and y,
(d) b and x,
(e) b and y.

2.

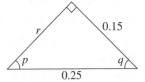

Find, expressing your answer as a fraction, the value of
(a) r,
(b) $\sin p \cos q$,
(c) $\tan p - \tan q$,
(d) $\sin^2 p + \cos^2 p$.

3. (a) Find, in terms of x, the length of BC.
(b) Find, to one decimal place, the size of $A\hat{C}B$.

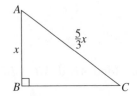

4. Given that $\tan 30° = \dfrac{\sqrt{3}}{3}$ and $\tan 60° = \sqrt{3}$, find the value of x and of y, leaving your answers in surd form.

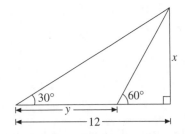

5. An equilateral triangle has sides of length 10 cm. Find
(a) its area, expressing your answer as a surd in its simplest form,
(b) the value of $\cos 60°$,
(c) the value of $\sin 30°$.

6. The figure shows a right-angled triangle ABC where $AB = (2x + 2)$ cm, $BC = (x - 4)$ cm and $AC = (2x + 3)$ cm.

(a) Using Pythagoras' Theorem, form an equation in x.

(b) Solve this equation and hence find the perimeter of $\triangle ABC$.

(c) Find, to one decimal place, the size of $B\hat{A}C$.

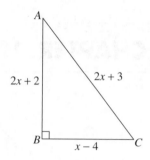

7.

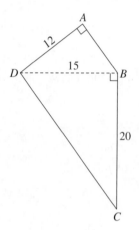

$ABCD$ is a quadrilateral with sides $AD = 12$ cm, $BC = 20$ cm and diagonal $BD = 15$ cm. If $B\hat{A}D = C\hat{B}D = 90°$, find

(a) the area and perimeter of $ABCD$,

(b) the size of $A\hat{B}D$ and $B\hat{D}C$, to one decimal place,

(c) what type of quadrilateral $ABCD$ is. Give reasons to support your answer.

8. Find AE if $AB = BC = CD = DE = 2$ cm.

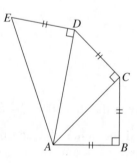

9. In the diagram, $AB = 9$ cm, $AC = 6.4$ cm, $AN = 3.6$ cm and $N\hat{A}D = 34°$. Calculate

(a) AD,

(b) $A\hat{B}N$,

(c) CD.

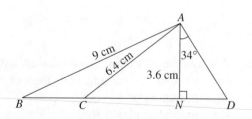

108

10.

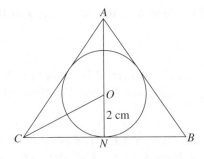

A circle centre O and radius 2 cm is inscribed in an equilateral triangle ABC and touches the side BC at N. Calculate

(a) CO,
(b) AN,
(c) AC,
(d) CN.

11.

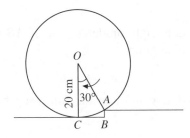

The diagram shows a wheel, centre O, which is in contact with the horizontal ground at C and is touching a vertical step AB at A. The radius of the wheel is 20 cm and $A\hat{O}C = 30°$. Calculate

(a) the length of the arc AC,
(b) the length of the chord AC,
(c) the height of the step AB.

12.

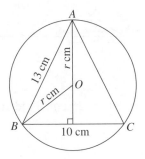

An isosceles triangle ABC is inscribed in a circle with centre O. If $AB = AC = 13$ cm and $BC = 10$ cm, find the radius, r cm, of the circle.

13. The sector in the figure has radius 9 cm and angle $250°$. It is folded up into a cone.

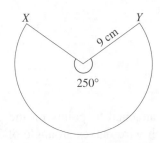
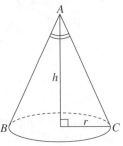

(a) Write down the length of the slant edge AC.
(b) Find, in terms of π, the length of the major arc XY.
(c) Find the radius, r, of the cone.
(d) Find the height, h, of the cone.
(e) Calculate the vertical angle BAC of the cone, giving your answer to one decimal place.

14. One diagonal of a rhombus is 24 cm. Find the length of the other diagonal if each side of the rhombus measures 13 cm.

15. *PQRS* is a rectangle in which *PQ* = 10 cm and *PS* = 6 cm. *T* is a point on *PQ* such that *RST* is an isosceles triangle whose equal sides are *RS* and *ST*. Find *RT*.

16. *PQRS* is a rectangle in which *PQ* = 9 cm and *PS* = 6 cm. *T* is a point on *PQ* such that *PT* = 7 cm and *RV* is the perpendicular from *R* to *ST*. Calculate *ST* and *RV*.

17. In parallelogram *ABCD*, the diagonal *AC* is at right angles to *AB*. If *AB* = 12 cm and *BC* = 13 cm, find the area of the parallelogram.

18. Find the unknown angles and sides marked *x*, *y* and *z* in the following figures.

    (a)

    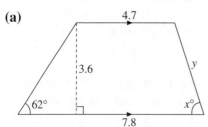

    (b)

    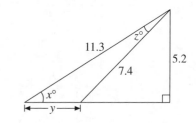

19.

    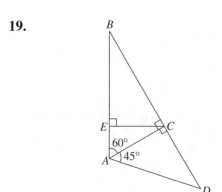

    In the figure, *AC* = 25 cm. Find the length of
    (a) *CE*,
    (b) *BE*,
    (c) *AB*.

20. An aerial mast is supported by four wires attached to points on the ground each 57 m away from the foot of the mast. If each wire makes an angle of 32° with the horizontal, find the height of the mast.

21. To find the width of a river, a boy places a wooden peg at a point *A* on one side directly opposite an object *B* on the opposite bank. From *A*, he walks 50 m along the bank to a point *C*. He observes that *A*$\hat{C}$*B* = 34°. Find the width of the river.

110

22. A ladder leans against a wall, touching a window sill, and makes an angle of 62° with the ground. Find the height of the window sill above the ground and the length of the ladder if the foot of the ladder is 3 m from the foot of the wall.

23. A 4 m plank rests on a wall 1.8 m high so that 1.2 m of it projects beyond the wall. Find
    (a) the angle the plank makes with the wall,
    (b) how far the foot of the ladder is from the foot of the wall.

24. A pendulum 45 cm long swings through a vertical angle of 30°. Find the height through which the pendulum bob rises.

25. A tree is x m high. The angle of elevation of its top from a point P on the ground is 23°. From another point Q, 10 m from P and in line with P and the foot of the tree, the angle of elevation is 32°. Find x.

26. The lower edge of a window of a house is 15 m above ground level. The angles of elevation of the top and bottom of the window are 27.4° and 23.25° respectively from a point K on level ground. Find the height of the window.

27. Jessica walked 10 m down a slope at an angle of depression of 60° and another 6 m down a slope at an angle of depression of 30°. How far is she below her initial point?

28. Two men, A and B, stand in line with a building. A stands 50 m from F, the foot of the building. The angle of elevation of T, the top of the building, from where A stands is 40°. Draw a diagram and calculate the distance from A that B should stand in order that the angle of elevation is 30°.

29. Two parallel chords in a circle of radius 7.5 cm measure 12 cm and 9 cm. They are on the same side of the circle.
    (a) Calculate the distance between them.
    (b) Find also the angle subtended at the centre by the chord of length 9 cm.

30. Find the angle subtended by a chord, AB, of length 16 cm at the centre, O, of a circle of radius 12 cm. Find also the area of the triangle OAB.

31. Two buildings on level ground are x m and 85 m tall. If the angle of elevation from the top of the shorter building to the top of the taller building is 32.92° and their distance apart is 54 m, find
    (a) the value of x, the height of the taller building,
    (b) the angle of depression from the top of the shorter building to the foot of the taller building.

32. From the top of a lighthouse 52 m high, the angles of depression of two ships, A and B, due east of it are 42° and 37° respectively, and the angle of depression of a ship, C, due west of it is 45°. How far apart are
    (a) the ships A and B,
    (b) the ships A and C?

33. Juliet was looking at Romeo from her balcony one evening. Romeo was standing at a distance of 10 m away from the foot of the house. When Juliet looked at Romeo's head, the angle of depression was 40°. When she looked at his toes, the angle of depression was 45°. How tall is Romeo?

34. In the diagram, $AD = 7$ cm, $AC = 13$ cm, $BC = 5$ cm and $A\hat{B}C = 90°$. Find
    (a) BD,
    (b) $\sin B\hat{A}C + \cos A\hat{C}B$,
    (c) $C\hat{D}B$,
    (d) $A\hat{C}D$.

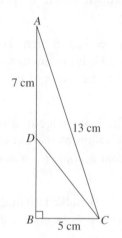

35. Two parallel chords of equal lengths are 24 cm apart. If the radius of the circle is 15 cm, find
    (a) the length of a chord,
    (b) the angle subtended by a chord at the centre of the circle.

36. In the diagram, CA is produced to Y and CB is produced to X. Given that
    $\tan A\hat{B}C = \dfrac{5}{12}$, $\cos A\hat{B}C = \dfrac{12}{13}$ and $\sin A\hat{B}C = \dfrac{5}{13}$,
    (a) calculate (i) AC if $AB = 52$,
    (ii) BC if $AC = 7.5$,
    (b) write down the value
    (i) $\sin A\hat{B}X$,
    (ii) $\cos A\hat{B}X$,
    (iii) $\tan B\hat{A}Y$.

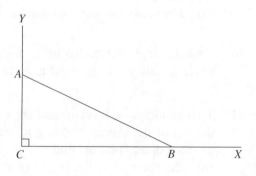

37.

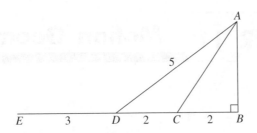

In the figure, $A\hat{B}C = 90°$, $AD = 5$ cm, $BC = CD = 2$ cm and $DE = 3$ cm. Find
(a) the area of $\triangle ACD$,
(b) the value of
  (i) $\cos C\hat{D}A$,
  (ii) $\tan A\hat{C}D$,
  (iii) $\sin A\hat{D}E$.

38.

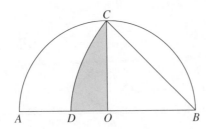

The figure shows a semicircle of radius 3 cm with centre O. The radius OC is perpendicular to the diameter AB. An arc of a circle is drawn with centre B and radius BC, intersecting AB at D. Find
(a) the length of OD,
(b) angle OBC,
(c) the area of the shaded region, leaving your answer in terms of π.

1. Copy and draw on graph paper, the reflection of each figure with respect to the mirror line XY.

(a)

(b)

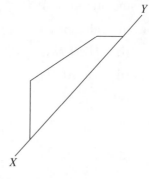

(c)

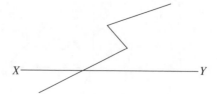

2. Use geometrical instruments to construct the image of each figure under reflection with respect to XY. Label the image.

(a)

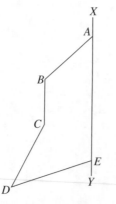

(b)

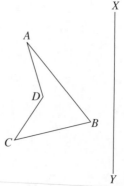

(c)

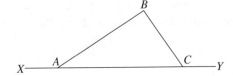

3. Copy the following figures. Construct the image of each figure under reflection in the line *l*.

   (a)

   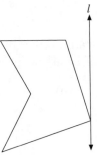

   (b)

   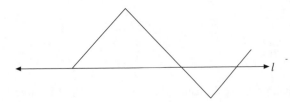

   (c)

   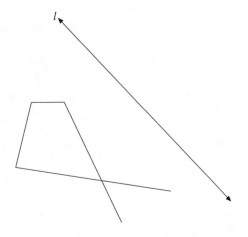

4. Copy the following figures. Construct the image of each figure under rotation through the given angle and direction about *P*.

(a)

(b)

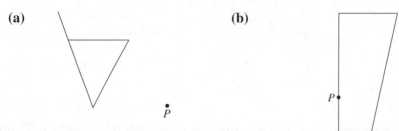

Through 90° anticlockwise.

Through 150° clockwise.

5. Copy the following figures. Construct the image of each figure under an enlargement with *X* as the centre of enlargement and with the given scale factor.

(a)

(b)

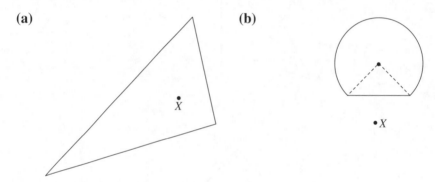

Enlarge by scale factor $\frac{1}{3}$.

Enlarge by scale factor −2.

6. Copy the following figures on graph paper. Draw and label the image of each figure under the transformation as instructed. Give the coordinates of the images of the vertices in each case.

(a)

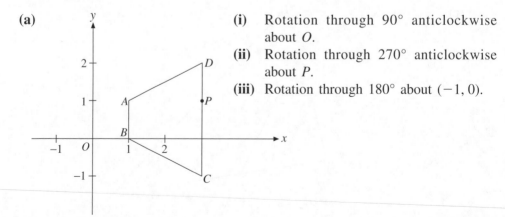

(i) Rotation through 90° anticlockwise about *O*.

(ii) Rotation through 270° anticlockwise about *P*.

(iii) Rotation through 180° about (−1, 0).

(b) **(i)** Translation -2 units in the y-direction.

    (ii) Translation 3 units in the x-direction and 4 units in the y-direction.

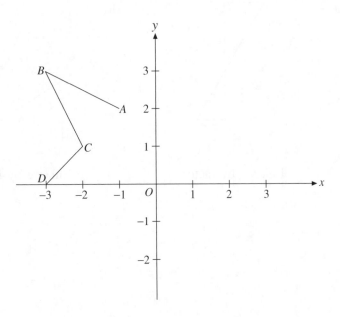

(c) Enlargement with centre at origin and with scale factor

    (i) $\dfrac{1}{3}$,

    (ii) $\dfrac{5}{2}$.

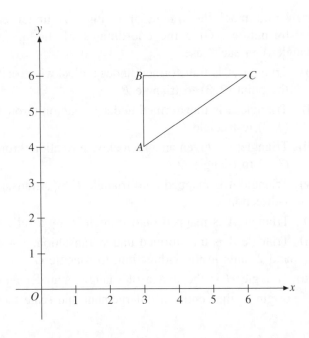

7. Copy the following figures. With X as the centre of enlargement, enlarge each figure with the scale factor given.

(a)

(b)

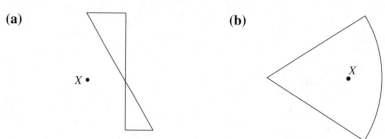

Enlarge by factor $\dfrac{7}{3}$.

Enlarge by factor $\dfrac{1}{2}$.

8. Answer the whole of this question on a sheet of graph paper.
The triangle A has vertices $(1, 4)$, $(2, 2)$ and $(3, 3)$.

   (a) Using a scale of 2 cm to represent 1 unit on each axis, draw axes for values of x and y in the ranges $-3 \leqslant x \leqslant 5$ and $-3 \leqslant y \leqslant 6$.
   Draw triangle A.

   (b) Draw and label the image of triangle A under each of the following transformations. Give the coordinates of the images of the vertices of triangle A in each case.

   (i) Triangle A is transformed under a clockwise rotation through $90°$ about the point $(2, 3)$ to triangle B.

   (ii) Triangle A is transformed under a rotation through $180°$ about the point $(3, 3)$ to triangle C.

   (iii) Triangle A is given an anticlockwise rotation through $90°$ about the point $(3, 1)$ to triangle D.

   (iv) Triangle A is mapped onto triangle E by a translation of -5 units in the y-direction.

   (v) Triangle A is mapped onto triangle F by a reflection in the y-axis.

   (vi) Triangle A is transformed under translation, -4 units in the x-direction and 2 units in the y-direction, to triangle G.

   (vii) Triangle H is the image of triangle A under an enlargement, with the origin as the centre of enlargement and scale factor $\dfrac{1}{2}$.

9. Describe fully the single transformation that maps
   (a) figure A onto B,
   (b) figure A onto C,
   (c) figure C onto D,
   (d) figure E onto B.

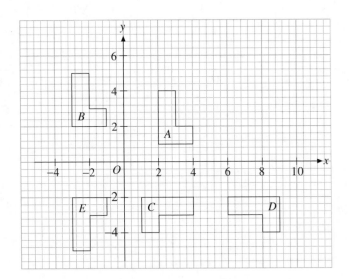

10. Under a translation T, the point (3, 1) is mapped onto the point (5, 4). What is the image of
    (a) the point (2, 5),
    (b) the point (0, 1),
    (c) the point (−2, −3).

11. Without plotting the points, write down the coordinates of the images of the following points when
    (i) reflected in the x-axis,
    (ii) reflected in the y-axis,
    (iii) translated −2 units along the x-axis,
    (iv) translated 3 units along the y-axis,
    (v) translated 1 unit in the x-direction and −4 units in the y-direction.
    (a) (2, −3)
    (b) (0, 6)
    (c) (−5, 0)

12.

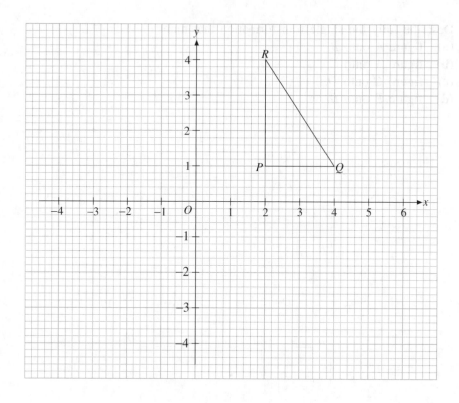

The triangle PQR with vertices $P(2, 1)$, $Q(4, 1)$ and $R(2, 4)$ is mapped onto $\triangle XYZ$ under a rotation of $180°$ about the origin; which is then mapped onto $\triangle ABC$ under a reflection in the y-axis.

(a) Draw the two image figures, $\triangle XYZ$ and $\triangle ABC$, and write down the coordinates of the vertices.

(b) Describe a single transformation which maps $\triangle PQR$ directly onto $\triangle ABC$.

13. Answer the whole of this question on a sheet of graph paper.
Using a scale of 2 cm to 1 unit on each axis, draw x and y axes for $-4 \leqslant x \leqslant 4$ and $-4 \leqslant y \leqslant 4$.

(a) The vertices of $\triangle ABC$ are $A(1, 1)$, $B(2, 2)$ and $C(0, 3)$. Draw and label $\triangle ABC$.

(b) $\triangle ABC$ is transformed under a rotation of $90°$ anticlockwise about the origin to $\triangle A_1B_1C_1$, followed by a translation, -1 unit in the x-direction and 1 unit in the y-direction, to $\triangle A_2B_2C_2$.

    (i) Draw and label $\triangle A_1B_1C_1$ and $\triangle A_2B_2C_2$ and write down the coordinates of the vertices.

    (ii) Describe fully a transformation which maps $\triangle ABC$ to $\triangle A_2B_2C_2$.

(c) $\triangle A_1B_1C_1$ is also mapped onto $\triangle A_3B_3C_3$. The vertices of $\triangle A_3B_3C_3$ are $A_3(1, -1)$, $B_3(2, -2)$ and $C_3(0, -3)$.

    (i) Draw and label $\triangle A_3B_3C_3$.

    (ii) Describe fully the transformation which maps $\triangle A_1B_1C_1$ onto $\triangle A_3B_3C_3$.

    (iii) Describe fully the single transformation which maps $\triangle ABC$ onto $\triangle A_3B_3C_3$.

14.

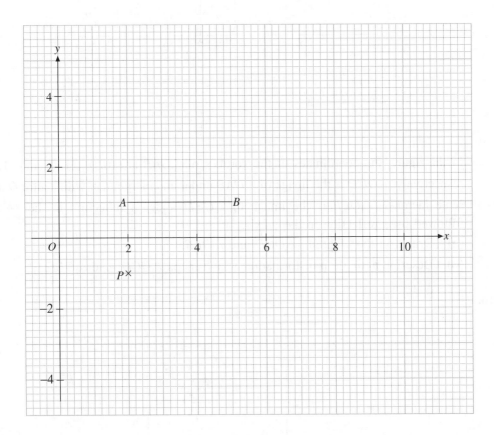

The diagram shows the line AB with coordinates $(2, 1)$ and $(5, 1)$.

(a) AB is mapped onto A_1B_1 by an enlargement centre O and scale factor $2\frac{1}{2}$.

Draw and label the line A_1B_1. State the coordinates of A_1 and B_1.

(b) A clockwise rotation of $90°$ about $P(2, -1)$ maps AB onto XY. Draw the line XY and state the coordinates of X and Y.

15.

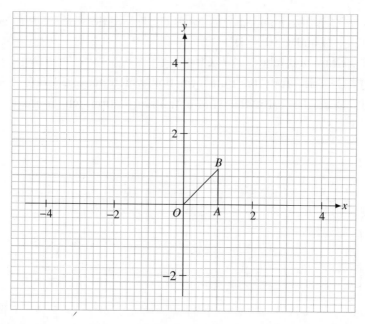

In the figure, the coordinates of the vertices of △OAB are (0, 0), (1, 0) and (1, 1) respectively. △OCD is the image of △OAB under an enlargement with centre O and scale factor 3. △OEF is the image of △OCD under a reflection in the x-axis, followed by a reflection in the y-axis.

(a) Draw, on the diagram, △OCD and △OEF.

(b) Describe a single transformation which maps △OCD onto △OEF.

16.

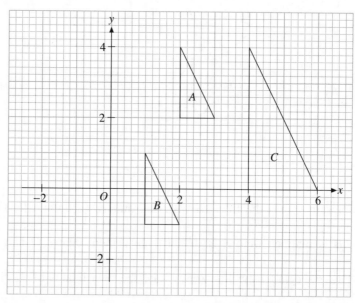

The transformation P maps triangle A onto triangle B. The transformation Q maps triangle B onto triangle C. The transformation R maps triangle A onto triangle C. Describe fully the transformations P, Q and R.

17.

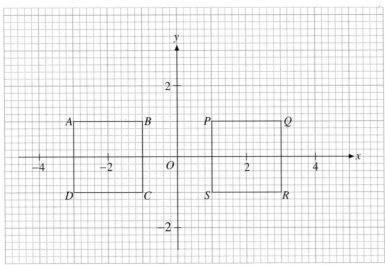

In each of the following cases, describe completely the single transformation which maps

(a) *ABCD* onto *PQRS*,

(b) *ABCD* onto *QPSR*,

(c) *ABCD* onto *RSPQ*,

(d) *ABCD* onto *SPQR*.

18. △*ABC* is given a transformation P followed by a transformation Q. Its two successive images are △*A'B'C'* and △*A"B"C"* respectively.

(a) Describe fully transformation P and transformation Q.

(b) Describe a single transformation equivalent to the combined transformations, P followed by Q.

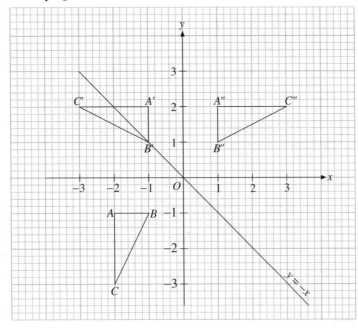

19.

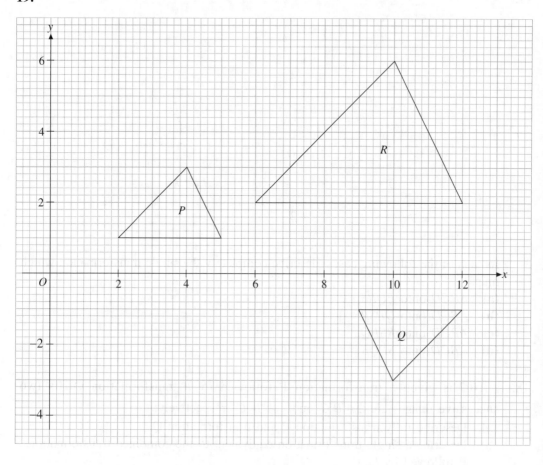

(a) *P* can be mapped onto *Q* by a rotation. State
    (i)   the coordinates of its centre of rotation,
    (ii) the angle of rotation.

(b) *P* can be mapped onto *R* by an enlargement. Find
    (i)   the coordinates of the centre of enlargement,
    (ii) its scale factor.

(c) *P* is transformed under translation, 2 units in the *x*-direction and −4 units in the *y*-direction, to *S*. Draw the image *S* and write down its coordinates.

20.

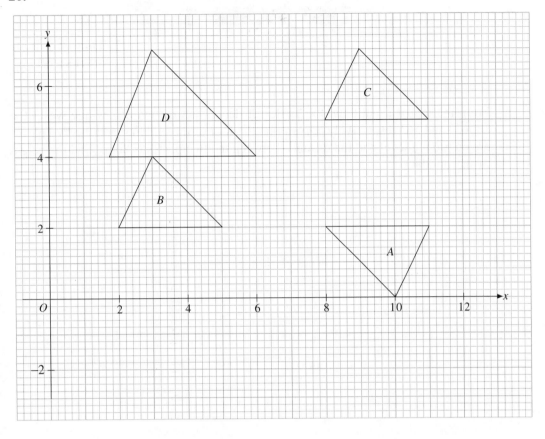

(a) Triangle *A* can be mapped onto triangle *B* under a certain transformation P. Triangle *C* is the image of triangle *B* under another transformation Q.

    (i) Describe fully transformations P and Q.

    (ii) Describe a single transformation which maps triangle *A* onto triangle *C*.

(b) Describe fully the single transformation which maps triangle *B* onto triangle *D*.

1. From the top of a building, the angles of depression of two places due west of it are 63° and 56° respectively. Given that the foot of the building and the two places are on ground level and the distance between the two places is 80 m, find the height of the building. [10]

Ans _____

2. Find x in each of the following. Give your answers correct to three significant figures.

   (a) $x = \cos 47.3°$ [1]

   (b) $\sin x° = 0.289\ 7$ [1]

   (c) $x \cos 62° = \sin 73° \times \tan 13°$ [2]

   (d) $\cos 30° (\tan x° + \sin 48.2°) = \cos 12.9°$ [3]

Ans (a) _____

      (b) _____

      (c) _____

      (d) _____

3. In the figure, $AD = 5$, $AC = 9.5$, $A\hat{B}C = 67°$ and $A\hat{D}C = 90°$. Find, to three significant figures,

   (a) $C\hat{A}D$,

   (b) AB,

   (c) BC.

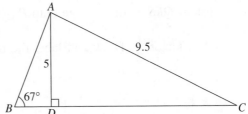

[9]

Ans (a) _____

      (b) _____

      (c) _____

4. On a piece of graph paper, and using a scale of 2 cm to 1 unit on both axes, draw the rectangle *PQRS* whose coordinates are *P*(0, 0), *Q*(4, 0), *R*(4, 2) and *S*(0, 2) and the rectangle *ABCD* whose coordinates are *A*(1, 4), *B*(1, 0), *C*(3, 0) and *D*(3, 4).

[3]

(a) Draw the axis of symmetry of the figure formed by the rectangles and write down its equation.

[1]

Ans _____

(b) Given that *PQRS* can be mapped onto *ABCD* under a transformation X, describe fully transformation X.

[2]

Ans _____

(c) *PQRS* is transformed onto *P'Q'R'S'* by an enlargement, centre (2, 3) and scale factor $\frac{1}{2}$. Draw and label the rectangle *P'Q'R'S'*.

[2]

(d) *PQRS* is mapped onto *P"Q"R"S"* under a 90° anticlockwise rotation about *P*. Draw and label the rectangle *P"Q"R"S"*.

[2]

(e) Describe fully the transformation that maps
    (i) rectangle *ABCD* onto *R"S"PQ"*, [2]
    (ii) rectangle *ABCD* onto *Q"PS"R"*. [2]

Ans (i) _____

    (ii) _____

5. In the diagram, $\triangle ABC$ is given a transformation P followed by a transformation Q. Its two successive images are $\triangle A_1B_1C_1$ and $\triangle A_2B_2C_2$ respectively. $\triangle A_3B_3C_3$ is the image of $\triangle A_1B_1C_1$ under a transformation R.

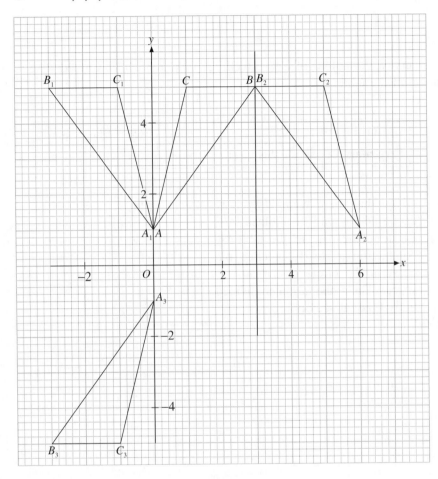

(a) Describe fully transformations P, Q and R. [6]

Ans _____

_____

_____

(b) Describe a single transformation equivalent to the combined transformations
(i) P followed by Q,
(ii) P followed by R. [4]

Ans (i) _____

(ii) _____

1. In a survey, the colour of cars travelling down a street was noted. The results are shown in the table.

Colour	Yellow	Red	Blue	Black
Percentage of cars of this colour	50%	25%	10%	x

(a) Given that there were 20 yellow cars, find the number of black cars.

(b) Illustrate the data in the table by completing a clearly labelled pie chart in the circle in the answer space. (The circle has been divided into 10 equal sectors.)

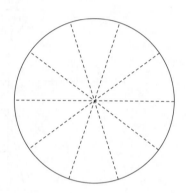

2.

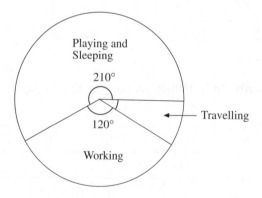

The pie chart shows how Jeremy spends each 24 hours of a day. Calculate

(a) the angle of the sector labelled 'Travelling',

(b) the number of hours Jeremy works each day,

(c) the percentage of time he spends travelling each day,

(d) the ratio of the number of hours he spends working to the number of hours he spends playing and sleeping.

3. The table shows the grades obtained by a group of Secondary Two students in a Science quiz.

Grades	A	B	C	D	E
No. of students	55	30	12	3	0

(a) How many students took part in the Science quiz?
(b) What percentage of the students obtained grade *C*?
(c) Which grade occurs most often?
(d) Represent the above data by
   (i) a bar chart, (ii) a pie chart, (iii) a line graph.
(e) In your opinion, describe in general terms any peculiar features of the line graph.

4. The number of children per family in a housing block is shown below.

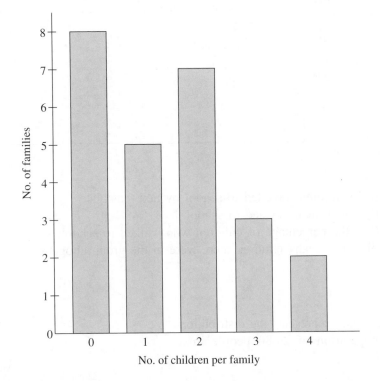

No. of children per family

(a) Name the statistical method that is employed to present the findings.
(b) How many families have only one child?
(c) How many families have less than three children?
(d) How many families have at least two children?
(e) How many children are there altogether?
(f) How many families are there altogether?
(g) What is the mean number of children per family?

5. A group of children were asked how they travel to school. The information they gave is represented on the pie chart.

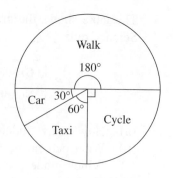

(a) Represent the same information by completing the bar chart in the answer space.

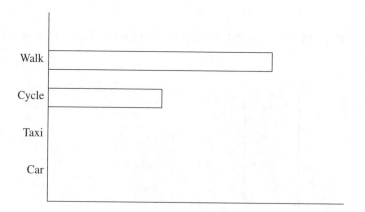

(b) If 20 children travelled to school by taxi, calculate
   (i) how many cycled to school,
   (ii) the percentage of children who walked to school,
   (iii) how many children there were in the group altogether.

6. The pie chart represents the distribution of a population of 2 880 people in a village.
Find
   (a) x if the number of boys is 432,
   (b) y if 22.5% of the population are girls,
   (c) w if there are twice as many women as men,
   (d) the number of females in the village.

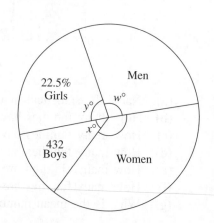

7. A factory produces three products *A*, *B* and *C* in the ratio $1 : x : 5$. When the output is illustrated by a pie chart, the angle of the sector representing the output of *C* is 120°. Find *x*.

8. A survey was conducted to find out the favourite type of sports 720 students enjoy in a certain school. The results are tabulated as follows:

Favourite sport	No. of students
Badminton	136
Basketball	180
Hockey	84
Soccer	212
Table-Tennis	108
Total	720

(a) Illustrate the results by
  (i) a bar chart,
  (ii) a pie chart.
(b) **(i)** Which diagram shows most clearly that one-quarter of the students like basketball?
  (ii) Which diagram best shows that table-tennis is more popular than hockey?
(c) What percentage of the students prefer badminton?
(d) What is the angle of the sector that represents the number of students who prefer soccer?

9. The pie chart shows the composition of a certain brand of milk powder.

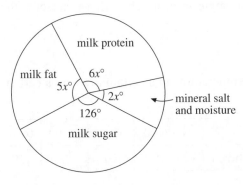

(a) Calculate the value of *x*.
(b) What is the percentage of milk protein in the milk powder?
(c) Given that one tin of milk powder contains 875 g of milk sugar, find the weight of the tin of milk powder.

10. Benjamin has a bottle of coins. The bar chart shows the number of 1¢, 5¢, 10¢, 20¢, 50¢ and $1 coins that Benjamin has in the bottle.

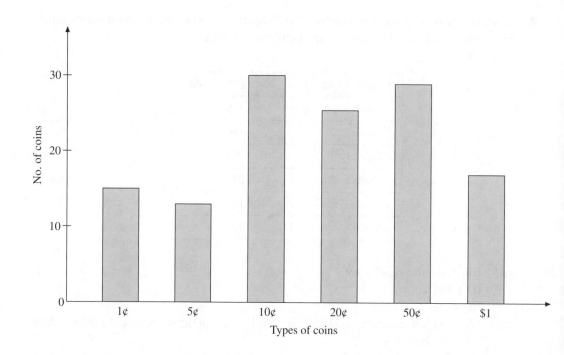

   (a)   Calculate the total number of coins in the bottle.
   (b)   Calculate the amount of money that Benjamin has in the bottle.
   (c)   How many more 20¢-coin are there than $1-coins?
   (d)   What is the percentage of 1¢-coins in the bottle?
   (e)   What percentage of the amount of money do the 50¢-coins make up?
   (f)   Find the angle in a pie chart that represents the number of 10¢-coins in the bottle.

11. The hourly temperatures in a certain town on a certain day are tabulated as follows:

Time	06 00	07 00	08 00	09 00	10 00	11 00	12 00
Temperature (°C)	18	20	23	27	29	32	34

Using a scale of 2 cm to represent 1 hour on the horizontal axis and 2 cm to represent 5 degrees Celsius on the vertical axis, draw a line graph to represent this data.

12. The bar chart shows the sales of the food, clothing and household sections of a departmental store for the years 1995 to 1997.

Food

Clothing

Household

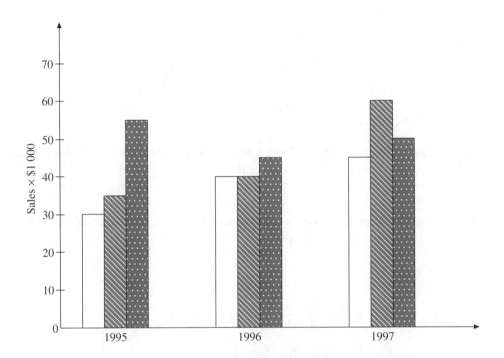

(a) How much were the sales of food items in 1995?

(b) What were the total sales of clothings from 1995 to 1997?

(c) Which item had the greatest amount of sales from 1995 to 1997?

(d) What fraction of the total sales of the store in 1997 did the sales of household items make up?

(e) What fraction of the total sales of the store from 1995 to 1997did the sales of food items make up?

(f) What fraction of the total sales of clothing from 1995 to 1997 did the sales of clothing in 1997 make up?

(g) What was the average sales per year of household items?

(h) What was the percentage increase in the sales of clothing from 1996 to 1997?

(i) Represent the sales of food items from 1995 to 1997 on a pie chart.

(j) Use a bar chart to illustrate the total sales of the store in each year from 1995 to 1996.

13. The pie chart shows how 40 lessons are allocated in a certain school.

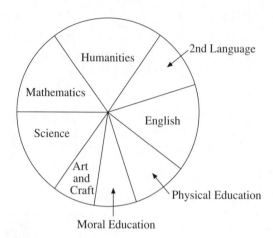

(a) Measure and write down the angles of the pie chart to the nearest degree.

(b) Calculate the number of lessons allocated for each subject.

14. The average number of packet drinks produced in the first four months of 1997 by a certain company are as follows:

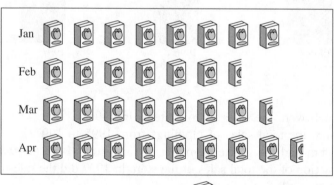

represents 5 000 packets

(a) What is the average number of packet drinks produced in the first four months of 1997?

(b) In which month was the least number of packet drinks produced?

(c) Find the percentage increase in the number of packet drinks produced from March to April.

CHAPTER 13 / Statistics II

1. The marks scored by 11 children in a spelling test are as follows:
   $$9, 1, 4, 8, 7, 8, 4, 2, 10, 9, 4$$
   Find, for this set of marks,
   (a) the mode, **(b)** the median, **(c)** the mean.

2. **(a)** Find the median of the following distribution.
   $$5.1, 7.9, 3.6, 2.1, 7.9, 4.2, 3.6, 7.8, 3.6$$

   (b) A footballer scored the following number of goals in 11 matches.
   $$1, 0, 0, 2, 2, 0, 1, 2, 3, 1, 2$$
   Write down the modal score.

   (c) A surveyor makes five separate measurements of the same angle and his results are:
   $$17.05°, 17.07°, 17.02°, 17.07°, 17.99°$$
   Calculate the mean of these readings.

3. A six-sided dice is thrown 29 times. The results are shown in the table below.

Number shown on dice	1	2	3	4	5	6
Frequency	8	7	5	2	3	4

   (a) For these results, write down
       (i) the mode, **(ii)** the median.
   (b) The dice is thrown one more time. Find the number shown on the dice if the mean of the 30 throws is to be exactly three.

4. The diagram illustrates the number of occupants per house for a sample of x houses in a certain district.
   (a) Present this information in a frequency table.
   (b) State the modal number of occupants per house.
   (c) Find x.
   (d) Calculate the mean number of occupants per house.
   (e) What percentage of the houses have more than two occupants?

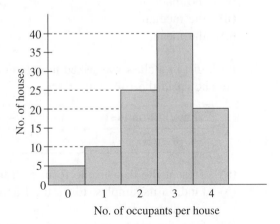

5. Firing at a target, a man can score 1, 2, 3, 4, 5 or 6. After 100 shots, his scores were as shown in the table below:

Score	1	2	3	4	5	6
No. of shots fired	26	15	14	15	18	x

   (a) Find x.
   (b) Present this data in the form of a histogram.
   (c) What are the mode and median of the distribution?
   (d) What is the mean score?

6. The histogram shows the distribution of 200 numbers from 1 to 6 inclusive.

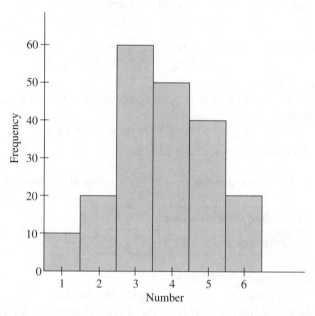

   From the distribution, find
   (a) the mode,
   (b) the median,
   (c) the mean.

7. Each girl in a class was asked how long it took her to solve a problem. The results are shown in the following table.

Time (in minutes)	$0 \leqslant x < 1$	$1 \leqslant x < 2$	$2 \leqslant x < 3$	$3 \leqslant x < 4$	$4 \leqslant x < 5$
No. of girls	5	5	8	7	5

   (a) Present the data in the form of a histogram.
   (b) Find, in its simplest form, the fraction of the class that solved the problem in less than 3 minutes.
   (c) Find the mode and median of the number of minutes required to solve the problem.

8. The following table gives the number of books borrowed by 100 people from a public library.

No. of books	3	4	5	6
No. of people	48	x	20	y

(a) Show that $x + y = 32$.

(b) Given that the mean number of books borrowed per person is 4.2, show that $2x + 3y = 88$.

(c) Solve the equations in (a) and (b) simultaneously to find the value of x and of y.

(d) State the modal number of books borrowed.

9. The following are the marks scored by 40 students in a Physics test marked out of a total of 10.

8	6	4	3	5	5	2	9	2	7
9	3	3	7	7	5	8	3	7	3
4	8	7	8	2	4	6	2	4	1
7	7	6	2	6	4	4	6	10	6

(a) Draw a frequency table and a histogram for the data.

(b) What is the average score?

(c) What is the most frequent score?

(d) What is the median score?

(e) What is the range, that is, the difference between the highest and the lowest scores?

10. The teachers of a certain school are asked to indicate the average number of hours they spend marking students' assignments each day. The following set of data is obtained.

6	4	3	1	2	2	3	1	4
1	2	5	3	4	5	2	2	3
3	1	2	2	3	1	4	2	

(a) Construct a frequency table and draw a histogram illustrating the results.

(b) How many teachers responded to the survey?

(c) What is the greatest number of hours spent marking?

(d) What is the most common number of hours spent marking?

(e) What is the percentage of teachers who spent at least 4 hours marking each day?

11. During an outbreak of flu in a city, the number of workers who reported sick in 10 successive days in a factory was illustrated by the following histogram.

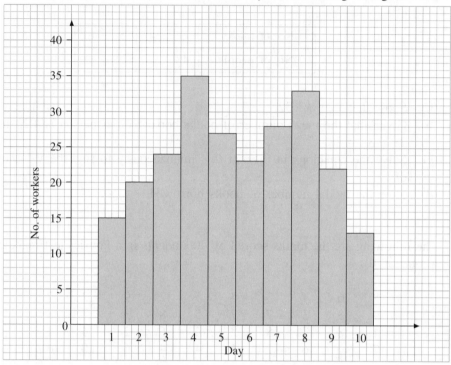

(a) How many workers reported sick on these 10 days?
(b) What is the average number of sick workers per day?
(c) On which day did the greatest number of workers report sick? How many workers reported sick on that day?
(d) On which days were the number of sick workers more than 30?

12. Two dice are tossed 30 times. The sum of the scores each time is shown below.

Score	2	3	4	5	6	7	8	9	10	11	12
Frequency	1	1	3	4	6	8	3	2	1	1	0

(a) Draw a histogram of the distribution.
(b) Find the mean, the median and the mode of the distribution.

13. The table below shows the frequency distribution of the number of mistakes made by each student in a spelling test in a class.

No. of mistakes	0	1	2	3	4	5	6	7
No. of students	3	7	10	6	5	3	1	1

(a) Draw a histogram to represent the data.
(b) What is the number of students in the class?
(c) What is the mode, median and mean of the distribution?

14. The mean of the masses of five parcels is 400 g. When another parcel is added, the mean of the masses increases by 7 g. Find the mass of the sixth parcel.

15. The mean of five numbers is 39. Two of the numbers are 103 and 35 and each of the other three numbers is equal to x.
Find
(a) the total of the five numbers,
(b) x.

16. The mean of a set of eight numbers is 3 and the mean of a different set of twelve numbers is x. Given that the mean of the combined set of twenty numbers is 9, calculate x.

17. The number of goals scored by a netball team in seven matches was 12, 23, 18, 14, 24, 25 and 12.
(a) Write down the mean score, the modal score and the median score.
(b) Find the number of goals the team needs to score in its next match in order that its mean score in the eight matches is exactly 17.

18. The mean of a set of eight numbers is 17.5. If six of the numbers are 12, 14, 15, 19, 24 and 25, find the mean of the other two numbers.

TEST PAPER 6

Time : 1 hour
Marks : 50

1. The bar chart illustrates the results of a survey carried out in some primary schools in a certain district.

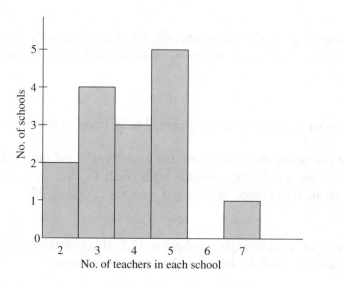

Calculate
(a) the total number of teachers in the district, [3]
(b) the percentage of schools which have five or more teachers, [2]
(c) the angle, in a pie chart, of the sector which represents schools with less than five teachers. [3]

Ans (a) _____

(b) _____

(c) _____

2.

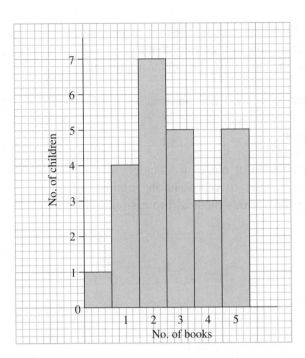

A group of 25 children were asked how many books they had read in the last month. The results of the survey are shown in the histogram.

(a) Present this information in a frequency table. [3]

(b) **(i)** How many children read not more than two books? [2]

   (ii) How many children read exactly five books? [1]

   (iii) What is the proportion of children who read more than three books? Give your answer as a fraction. [2]

(c) Find the total number of books read in the last month. [2]

(d) Find the mean, mode and median of the number of books read in the last month. [3]

Ans (a)

Ans (b) (i) _____

   (ii) _____

   (iii) _____

   (c) _____

   (d) _____

3. The pie chart illustrates the distribution of people in the medical profession in a certain country.

   (a) Calculate the angle of the sector representing Nurses. [2]
   (b) Given that there are 1 243 pharmacists, find the number of
      (i) doctors,
      (ii) dentists. [4]
   (c) What is the ratio of nurses to doctors? [2]
   (d) Draw a bar chart to represent the number of people in the various medical profession. [4]

Ans (a) _____

    (b) (i) _____

       (ii) _____

    (c) _____

4. The bar chart illustrates the means of travelling to school by a group of primary one pupils.

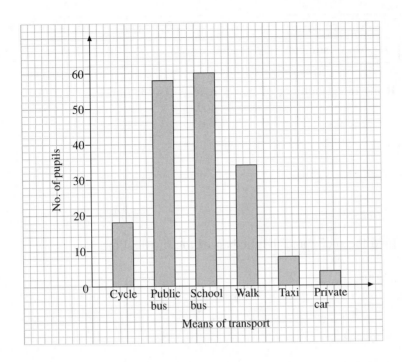

(a) Calculate
  (i) the total number of primary one pupils, [2]
  (ii) the percentage of pupils who do not travel to school by bus. [2]
(b) What is the most popular means of transport? [1]

Ans (a) (i) _____

(ii) _____

(b) _____

5. The following table shows the number of books read by a group of students in the previous year.

No. of books	0	1	2	3	4	5	6
No. of students	2	4	x	8	$2x$	7	4

(a) If the mean number of books read is 3.425, find x.　[5]

Ans ＿＿＿＿＿＿＿＿＿＿＿

(b) Find the mode and the median of the distribution.　[2]

Ans ＿＿＿＿＿＿＿＿＿＿＿

＿＿＿＿＿＿＿＿＿＿＿

(c) Draw a histogram to represent the data given in the table.　[5]

Ans (c)

CHAPTER 14 / More Algebraic Manipulations

1. Find the sum of
   (a) $2x^3 + 3x^2 + 1$, $2x^3 - 2x^2 + 6x$, $4x^2 - 2x + 9$, $-3x^3 + 5$,
   (b) $x^5 - 3x^4 + 5x^2 - 2x + 3$, $2x^5 + 7x^2 - 8$, $-3x^5 + 7x^4 - 4x^2 + 5x - 9$.

2. Subtract
   (a) $3x^2 + 2x - 4$ from $x^3 - 3x^2 - 5x + 6$,
   (b) $2a^5 + 3a^4 - 7a^3 + 4a^2 + 8$ from $2a^6 - 3a^5 - 7a^4 + 4a^3 - 8a^2 + 3a$.

3. From what polynomial must $(3p^2 + 2pq + 7q^2)$ be subtracted to give $(7p^2 + 5pq - 3q^2)$?

4. Subtract the sum of $(a^2 + 5ab + b^2)$ and $(2a^2 - 4ab + 5b^2)$ from the sum of $(5a^2 - 7ab + 4b^2)$ and $(7a^2 - 2ab + 3b^2)$.

5. Add $(-12a^3 - 3a^2 + 4a + 6)$ to $(2a^3 + 5a^2 - 7)$.

6. What polynomial must be added to $(2a^4 - 3a^3 + 2a^2 - a - 5)$ to give $(3a^4 - 4a^3 + 5a^2 + a - 11)$?

7. What polynomial must be subtracted from $(7x^3 + 2x^2 - 8x + 7)$ to give $(3x^2 - 4x - 9)$?

8. What polynomial must be subtracted from the sum of $(3a^2 + 4ab - 7b^2)$ and $(5a^2 + 4ab + 8b^2)$ to give $(11a^2 + ab + b^2)$?

9. From what polynomial must the sum of $(2x^3 + 7x^2 - 5x + 2)$ and $(7x^3 + 4x^2 - 5x + 7)$ be subtracted to give $(2x^3 - 4x^2 + 7x - 5)$?

10. Multiply $(4x^3 - 2x^2 + 1)$ by $(x^2 + 2x - 1)$.

11. Subtract the product of $(4x^2 - 2)(-3x^2 + 2x + 5)$ from $(x^4 + 8x^3 - x^2 - 4x - 5)$.

12. Divide $(15x^3 - x^2 - 26x - 12)$ by $(5x + 3)$.

13. Find the polynomial which when multiplied to $(3x - 4)$ gives $(3x^3 + 2x^2 - 11x + 4)$.

14. What polynomial must $(x + 2)$ divide to give $(4x^2 - 3x + 1)$?

15. Find the polynomial which has a quotient of $(2x^3 + x^2 + 3x + 6)$ and a remainder of 13 when divided by $(x - 2)$.

16. Show that $(x^3 - 7x^2 + 4x + 12)$ is divisible by $(x + 1)$.

17. Find the divisor of the polynomial $(2x^3 + 3x^2 - 11x - 6)$ if
    (a) the quotient is $(2x^2 + 7x + 3)$ and the remainder is 0,
    (b) the quotient is $(2x^2 - x - 9)$ and the remainder is 12.

18. Simplify the following expressions.
    (a) $3(4x^2 + 5)(x^3 - 2x - 1) - x^2(x - 2)(x^2 + x + 3)$
    (b) $4(3x + 1)^2(3x - 1) + 2(x^2 - 4x - 3)(x^2 + 4x + 3)$
    (c) $(x^2 - x + 1)(x^2 + x - 1) - (x - 1)(1 - x)$
    (d) $(a - w)(b - w)(c - w) \ldots (y - w)(z - w)$

19. Do the following divisions. State the results in the form:
dividend $=$ divisor $\times$ quotient $+$ remainder.
    (a) $(18x^3 + 4x^2 - 12x) \div 3x$
    (b) $(3x^4 - x^2 + 8x - 4) \div (x + 1)$
    (c) $(4x^4 - 5x^3 + x^2 - 2) \div (x^2 - x + 2)$
    (d) $(x^4 + 2x^3 - 2x^2 - 2x + 4) \div (x^3 - x^2 + x - 1)$
    (e) $(4x^3 - 4x + 3) \div (2x - 1)$
    (f) $(3x^3 - 7) \div (x - 3)$
    (g) $(8x^4 - x^2 + 5) \div (2x^2 + 2x - 1)$

20. For the following identities, find the values of the unknown constants.
    (a) $2x^2 + ax - 1 \equiv bx^2 + 3x + c$
    (b) $2x^2 - 5x + 3 \equiv (x - 1)(ax + b)$
    (c) $x^3 - 2x^2 + 5 \equiv ax(x - 1)^2 + b(x - 1) + c$
    (d) $a(x - 2) + b(x - 4) \equiv x + 2$
    (e) $3x^2 + 6x - 4 \equiv p(x - q)^2 + r$
    (f) $x^2 + x + A \equiv (x + A)(x - 1) + B$
    (g) $x^3 + ax^2 + 4x + b \equiv (x - c)(x^2 - x + 3) + 6$
    (h) $(ax + b)(x - 2) + c(x^2 + 3) \equiv 14$

21. If $y = 3x - 1$ and $y = \dfrac{5 - 2z}{4}$, express

    (a) x in terms of y,   **(b)** z in terms of y,
    (c) x in terms of z,   **(d)** z in terms of x.

22. If $y = \dfrac{4x + 3}{12}$ and $z = 2x + 1$, express

    (a) x in terms of z,
    (b) y in terms of z.

23. If $x = 4 - 7y$ and $y = \frac{2}{3}z + 9$, express

    (a) x in terms of z,

    (b) z in terms of y.

24. If $y = 1 + \frac{4}{3}y$ and $z = \frac{3x - 1}{2}$, express

    (a) y in terms of x,

    (b) x in terms of z,

    (c) y in terms of z.

25. If $x = \frac{1 - 3y}{7}$ and $z = \frac{1 - 7x}{3}$, express

    (a) x in terms of z,

    (b) y in terms of z.

26. If $x = 1 - y$, $y = 1 - z$ and $z = 1 - w$, express w in terms of x.

27. If $x = 5 - 3y$, $y = 4z + 1$ and $z = \frac{w - 2}{3}$, express x in terms of w.

28. Simplify the following expressions.

    (a) $(4x^3 - 2x^2 - 2x - 1) - 6x(2 - 3x + x^2) + 2(x^3 - 8x^2 + 4)$

    (b) $(7m^4 - 2m^2 + 1)(3m - 3) + (4m^3 + 2m - 1)(3m^2 - 2)$

29. Multiply $(3a^2 - 1)$ by $2a^3$. Subtract the result from the sum of $(2a^5 + a^4 - 2a - 1)$ and $(4a^5 - 5a^3 - 6a^2 + 7a - 3)$.

30. Find the quotient and the remainder of each of the following.

    (a) Divide $(4x^4 + x^2 - 5x)$ by $(2x + 1)$.

    (b) Divide $(x^4 + 5x^3 - 3x^2 + x - 1)$ by $(x^2 + 2x - 3)$.

31. Find the values of the unknowns in each of the following.

    (a) $(3x + 2)(2 - 3x) \equiv ax^2 + bx + 4$

    (b) $6x^3 + ax^2 - 3x + 2 \equiv (bx + c)(2x^2 - 1)$

32. If $y = 4 - \frac{x}{3}$ and $y = \frac{7z + 2}{3}$,

    (a) express

        (i) x in terms of y,

        (ii) x in terms of z,

    (b) find the value of x and of y if $z = 0.4$.

FINAL TERM ASSESSMENT PAPER 1

Time : $\frac{3}{4}$ hour

Marks : **40**

ALL questions may be attempted.

Answers are to be written on the question paper in the spaces provided.

Omission of essential workings will result in loss of marks. No calculators are allowed.

This paper consists of 15 questions.

1. Find the value of a and of b in the identity $ax(2x - b) = 2x(x + 1)$. [3]

Ans _____

2. Find the mode and median of the following set of scores.

$$3, 7, 5, 8, 7, 6, 3, 7, 8$$ [2]

Ans _____

3.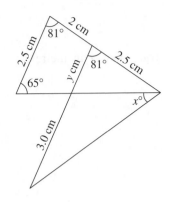

Find x and y in the following pairs of congruent triangles. [2]

Ans $x =$ _____

$y =$ _____

4. Factorise $3x^2 + 10x - 48$. [2]

Ans _____

5. Simplify $\dfrac{1}{2(x-3)} + \dfrac{2}{3x-1}$. [3]

Ans _____

6.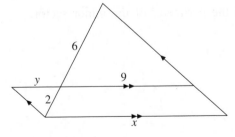

Find the value of x and of y. [3]

Ans $x =$ _____

$y =$ _____

7. A car travels 108 km in 3 hours.
   (a) Express the speed in km/h. [1]
   (b) How far does it travel in 40 s? Give your answer in metres. [2]

Ans (a) _____

   (b) _____

8. Solve $\dfrac{x}{4} - \dfrac{3x-4}{3} = \dfrac{1}{3}$. [3]

Ans _____

9.

Find the perimeter of the minor sector. [3]

Ans _____

10.

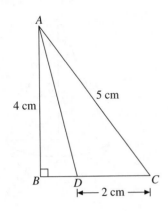

In the figure, $AB = 4$ cm, $AC = 5$ cm, $CD = 2$ cm and $A\hat{B}C = 90°$. Find

(a) BD,

(b) $\sin A\hat{C}B$,

(c) $\tan A\hat{D}B$. [3]

Ans (a) _____

(b) _____

(c) _____

11. Calculate the value of k if the line $x - 2y = 10$ passes through the point $(k, 3k)$. [2]

Ans _____

12. Find the volume of the solid, leaving your answer in terms of π.

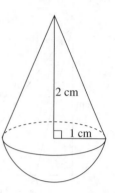

2 cm

1 cm

[3]

Ans _____

13.

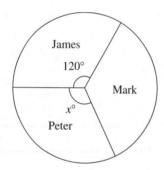

James 120°

Mark

$x°$

Peter

James, Mark and Peter have 3 000 stamps among them. Peter has 900 stamps. The pie chart represents the number of stamps each boy has.

(a) How many stamps does James have?

(b) Calculate the value of x.

(c) What fraction of stamps does Mark have?

[3]

Ans (a) _____

(b) _____

(c) _____

14. The volumes of two similar solid paper weights are in the ratio 8 : 27.

   (a) Find the ratio of their heights. [1]

   (b) The smaller paper weight has a mass of 16 g. What is the mass of the larger paper weight? [2]

Ans *(a)* _____

      (b) _____

15. Draw the image of the figure under reflection with respect to the line *XY*. [2]

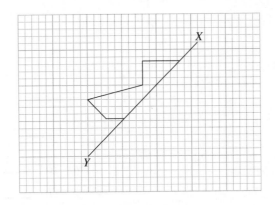

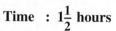
Time : $1\frac{1}{2}$ hours

Marks: **60**

This paper consists of 2 sections.

Section A consists of **6 questions.**

Section B consists of **5 questions**.

Calculators may be used in this paper. If the degree of accuracy is not specified and if the answer is not exact, the answer should be given to three significant figures.

Section A (28 marks)

ALL *questions may be attempted.*

1. Simplify $(1 + x - x^3)(1 + x^2) + x^2(x^2 - 1)(x + 1)$. [4]

Ans _____

2. If $y = \dfrac{3x - 5}{15}$ and $y = \dfrac{1 - 5z}{15}$, express
   - **(a)** x in terms of y, [2]
   - **(b)** x in terms of z. [3]

Ans (a) _____

(b) _____

3. Divide $3x^3 + 2x^2 - 8x - 5$ by $3x - 1$. Write down the quotient and the remainder.

[4]

Ans _____

4.

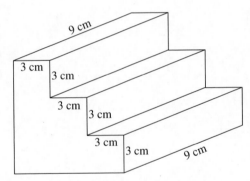

Find the total surface area of the prism.

[4]

Ans _____

5.

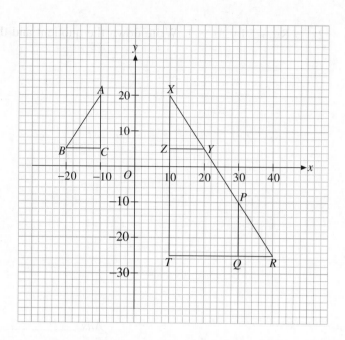

Describe fully the transformation that
(a) maps $\triangle ABC$ onto $\triangle XYZ$, [1]
(b) maps $\triangle XYZ$ onto $\triangle XRT$, [2]
(c) maps $\triangle XYZ$ onto $\triangle PRQ$. [2]

Ans (a) _____

_____

(b) _____

_____

(c) _____

_____

6. In Section B of the Mid-term Examination, the students were asked to answer six questions. The histogram shows the number of questions attempted by the students.

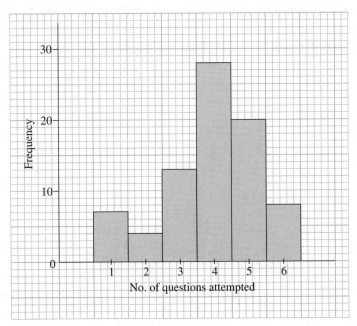

(a) How many students took the examination? [2]

(b) What percentage of the students attempted four questions or more? [2]

(c) Find the mean number of questions attempted. [2]

Ans (a) _____

(b) _____

(c) _____

1. A man stands on top of a cliff. The angle of elevation of the head of the man, as seen from a boat 78 m away, is 35°. The angle of elevation of the top of the cliff, as seen from the boat, is 34.2°. Find the height of the man. [8]

Ans _____

2.

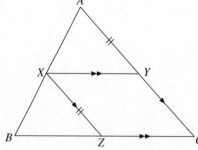

In the diagram, *XY // BC*, *XZ // AC* and *AY = XZ*.
(a) Name a pair of congruent triangles. State the case of congruency. [2]

Ans _____

(b) Name a pair of similar triangles. [1]

Ans _____

(c) Find the ratio of

    (i) $\dfrac{AX}{XB}$, [1]

    (ii) $\dfrac{XY}{BC}$, [1]

    (iii) $\dfrac{\text{area of } \triangle AXY}{\text{area of } \triangle ABC}$. [1]

Ans (i) _____

    (ii) _____

    (iii) _____

(d) If the area of $\triangle ABC$ is 16.8 cm^2, what is the area of quadrilateral $XYCZ$?
[2]

Ans _____

3. *OABC* is a rectangle. The width, *OA*, of the rectangle is 2 cm and the radius, *OY*, of the circle with centre *O* is 4 cm.
Find

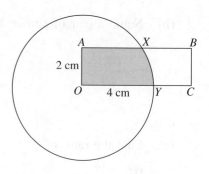

(a) $X\hat{O}Y$, [2]

(b) *AB*, [2]

(c) the area enclosed by the circle and the rectangle, i.e. the shaded area. [4]

Ans (a) _____

(b) _____

(c) _____

4. The following table shows the number of people in each car that passes a certain checkpoint.

No. of people per car	1	2	3	4	5	6
No. of cars	47	40	26	17	21	x

(a) Given that the average number of people per car is 2.7, find x.   [4]

Ans _____

(b) Find the median number of people per car.   [1]

Ans _____

(c) What percentage of the cars have less than three people in them?   [2]

Ans _____

(d) Find the size of the angle in a pie chart that represents the number of cars with two people in them.   [1]

Ans _____

5. Answer the whole of this question on a sheet of graph paper.

Triangle A has vertices (1, 1), (1, 1.5) and (2, 1.5).
Triangle B has vertices (0, 1.5), (0, 2.5) and (2, 2.5)

(a) Using a scale of 2 cm to represent 1 unit on each axis, draw axes for values of x and y in the ranges $-1 \leqslant x \leqslant 6$ and $-3 \leqslant y \leqslant 3$. Draw and label triangles A and B. [2]

(b) Find the scale factor and the centre of the enlargement which maps triangle A onto triangle B. [2]

Ans _____

(c) Triangle C has vertices (3, 0.5), (2, 0.5) and (2, 2.5).
    (i) Draw and label triangle C.
    (ii) Describe fully the transformation which maps triangle B onto triangle C. [2]

Ans (i) _____

    (ii) _____

(d) A translation of 3 units in the x-direction maps triangle A onto triangle D. Draw and label triangle D. [2]

ANSWERS

Chapter 1

1. (a) 3^{22} (b) $\dfrac{1}{14^6}$ (c) $\left(\dfrac{4}{3}\right)^4$ (d) 6^{21}

   (e) 7^{16} (f) $\dfrac{1}{6^6}$ (g) $\dfrac{1}{2^4}$ (h) $\dfrac{3}{2}$

   (i) 15^2

2. (a) $\dfrac{8}{125}$ (b) $\dfrac{1}{49}$ (c) 25 (d) $\dfrac{64}{125}$

   (e) $\dfrac{9}{4}$ (f) -1 (g) -64 (h) 64

   (i) $-\dfrac{1}{64}$ (j) $\dfrac{1}{64}$ (k) $-\dfrac{1}{27}$ (l) $\dfrac{1}{8}$

   (m) $\dfrac{8}{27}$ (n) 24 (o) 1 (p) $\dfrac{1}{4}$

   (q) 36 (r) $1\,011.01$

3. (a) $\dfrac{1}{128}$ (b) 216 (c) $\dfrac{3}{16}$ (d) $\dfrac{3}{2}$

   (e) $\dfrac{8}{27}$ (f) 10 (g) $\dfrac{97}{100}$ (h) $3\dfrac{1}{16}$

   (i) $2\dfrac{5}{8}$ (j) $\dfrac{1}{10}$ (k) $\dfrac{3}{5}$ (l) $\dfrac{1}{10}$

   (m) $\dfrac{7}{15}$ (n) $1\dfrac{1}{8}$ (o) 74

4. (a) 3^7 (b) 2^2 (c) $\left(\dfrac{2}{15}\right)^4$ (d) 3^{-32}

   (e) 2^4 (f) $\left(\dfrac{5}{7}\right)^{12}$ (g) $\left(\dfrac{3}{2}\right)^6$ (h) 2^6

   (i) 2^{17} (j) 1

5. (a) $\dfrac{1}{4}$ (b) 4 (c) $-\dfrac{1}{2}$ (d) 1

   (e) 1 (f) 15 (g) -33 (h) 23

6. (a) $x = -4,\ y = -1$ (b) $x = 2,\ y = \dfrac{4}{3}$

7. (a) a^5 (b) a^6 (c) $20a^{28}$ (d) $\dfrac{1}{2a^6}$

   (e) $\dfrac{4a^5}{3}$ (f) $\dfrac{1}{3}a^2b$ (g) $\dfrac{q^2}{p^3}$ (h) $\dfrac{27}{p^3}$

   (i) $\dfrac{5}{m^3}$ (j) $\dfrac{2y^8}{x^{10}}$ (k) $\dfrac{2}{a^2b^9}$ (l) a^{17}

   (m) $2a^5$ (n) $24a^6$ (o) $9a^2$ (p) $a^{13}b^6$

(q)	$\dfrac{243t^3}{s^2}$	(r)	$-a$	(s)	$-64a^3$	(t)	$\dfrac{1}{x^{14}y^{22}}$
(u)	$\dfrac{5}{2x^3y^2}$	(v)	$\dfrac{16b^6c^3}{3a^5}$	(w)	$\dfrac{32}{x^8y^6}$	(x)	$\dfrac{x^6}{2y^3}$
(y)	$\dfrac{3}{4m^2}$	(z)	$\dfrac{a^3}{b^4c^{n+1}}$				

8. (a) $-x^{12}$ (b) $-3x^8$ (c) a^3 (d) $16a^{-4}$

(e) 1 (f) z^{11} (g) $\dfrac{27}{4}a^2c^{11}$ (h) x^5

(i) a^9 (j) $p^{30}q^4r^{19}s^7$ (k) $3a^7b^{14}$ (l) ab^{-3}

(m) $p^{17}q^{-32}r^{12}$ (n) $a^{-9}b^2c^{-5}$ (o) 18

9. (a) -3 (b) -4 (c) $\dfrac{1}{3}$ (d) $-\dfrac{1}{3}$

(e) 8 (f) 7 (g) 7 (h) 0

(i) -2 (j) $\dfrac{3}{2}$ (k) $5\dfrac{1}{3}$ (l) $\dfrac{1}{9}$

(m) 3 (n) 1 (o) 1

10. (a) 6×10^{-3} (b) 3 (c) $\dfrac{3}{7}$ (d) -2

(e) $-\dfrac{1}{8}$ (f) $\dfrac{16}{49}$ (g) $-\dfrac{1}{5}$ (h) -1

(i) -1 (j) -2 (k) 2 (l) -1

(m) $-\dfrac{3}{4}$ (n) -2 (o) -2 (p) $-\dfrac{3}{5}$

(q) $\dfrac{1}{2}$ (r) 3 (s) -2 (t) 0

(u) $\dfrac{1}{2}$ (v) $\dfrac{1}{4}$ (w) $3\dfrac{1}{2}$ (x) $1\dfrac{1}{3}$

(y) $\dfrac{1}{2}$

11. (a) $0.002\,48$ (b) $412\,500$ (c) $2\,004$ (d) $8\,088.08$
(e) $0.000\,56$ (f) 0.039

12. (a) 2.34×10^4 (b) 5.089×10^{-3} (c) 1.71×10^{-1}
(d) $3.471\,7 \times 10^{-3}$ (e) 2.16×10^6 (f) 1.8×10^{-4}
(g) 1.8×10^5 (h) 4.78×10^{-5} **13.** 3.375×10^3

14. (a) 1.2×10^3 cm   (b) 6×10^{-7} km^2 (c) 1.25×10^{-4} kg
(d) 4.42×10^4 ml   (e) 5×10^5 cm^3

15. (a) 1.12×10^2 (b) $2.800\,04 \times 10^3$
(c) 7×10^4 (d) 2.775×10^3

16. (a) 0.040 (b) 6.4×10^{-5} (c) 0.01 **17.** 1.5×10^4

18. (a) 2.8×10^{-7}, 6.4×10^{-8}, 43×10^{-9}
(b) $2^5 \times 3^6 \times 7^5$, $2^4 \times 3^7 \times 7^5$, $2^3 \times 3^7 \times 7^6$

19. (a) 8×10^3 (b) 4×10^2

20. (a) 3.52×10^{-2} (b) 1.92×10^{-4} (c) 2.18×10^{13}
(d) 8.48×10^5 (e) 3.51×10^2 (f) 3.38×10^0

(g) 6.18×10^{-1} **(h)** 6.70×10^{-1} **(i)** 4.64×10^{-1}
(j) 5.15×10^{-3} **(k)** 3.67×10^{-2}

21. **(a)** 400 000 **(b)** **(i)** $3.95 \times 10^7\%$ **(ii)** 3.95×10^2 km
22. **(a)** $x = 0$ **(b)** $x = -2$

Chapter 2
1. **(a)** 89 975 **(b)** 2 500 **(c)** 597 **(d)** 7 290
   (e) 230 **(f)** 158 404 **(g)** 98 **(h)** 25
   (i) 2 **(j)** $\dfrac{1}{40}$ **(k)** $\dfrac{1}{160}$ **(l)** 2 460 005
   (m) 2 500

2. **(a)** 3.7 **(b)** 7, 19 **(c)** $3\dfrac{1}{2}$ **(d)** 14
   (e) 8.25 **(f)** **(i)** 9 **(ii)** 98 **(iii)** -63

3. **(a)** $\dfrac{29a - 15}{20}$ **(b)** $\dfrac{3x + 39y + 4}{12}$ **(c)** $\dfrac{11x - 13}{20}$
   (d) $\dfrac{17x - 74}{60}$ **(e)** $\dfrac{2y^2 - 3 + 4x^2}{xy}$ **(f)** $\dfrac{4a - 3}{2a^2}$
   (g) $-\dfrac{1}{4x}$ **(h)** $\dfrac{a + 2x}{3a}$ **(i)** $\dfrac{6xy}{5}$
   (j) 0 **(k)** $\dfrac{2(a - c)}{ac}$ **(l)** $\dfrac{9x + 2}{(x - 2)(x + 2)}$
   (m) $\dfrac{x - y}{(x + 1)(y + 1)}$ **(n)** $\dfrac{55x + 70}{6(x - 2)(x + 2)}$ **(o)** $\dfrac{2(6c + 5d)}{15(2c - d)}$
   (p) $\dfrac{-9r}{3q + 3r}$ **(q)** $\dfrac{5a + 7}{6(a - 4)}$ **(r)** $\dfrac{3}{3 + 2a}$
   (s) $\dfrac{-9r}{(p + 3r)(p - 3r)}$ **(t)** $\dfrac{2m}{2m - 1}$ **(u)** $\dfrac{7}{6(e - f)}$
   (v) $\dfrac{5}{x}$ **(w)** $\dfrac{x(x - 1)}{x + 2}$ **(x)** $\dfrac{2}{x - 1}$
   (y) $\dfrac{5}{x + 2}$ **(z)** $\dfrac{3}{x(x + 5)}$

4. **(a)** $2x - 21$ **(b)** $32x^2 - 4x^5$ **(c)** $15p^2 - 2p - 8$
   (d) $8 + 26k - 7k^2$ **(e)** $8a + 6$ **(f)** $18a^2 - 3a - 6$
   (g) $5m^3 + 10m^2n^2 - mn - 2n^3$ **(h)** $2x^3 - 9x^2 - 20x - 3$
   (i) $3u^4 + 2u^3 + 4u^2 + u + 2$ **(j)** $-x^2 - 14x + 3$
   (k) $x^4 + 3x^3 - 3x^2 - 9x$ **(l)** $3a^5 - a^4 - 18a^3 + 6a^2$
   (m) $-15x^2 + 10x - 30$ **(n)** $10x + 6$ **(o)** $5 + 3x - 8x^2$
   (p) $16x^2 + 48x$ **(q)** $40x - 48x^2 - 64x^3$ **(r)** $6 + m - 9m^2$
   (s) $2x^3 - 5x^2 - 3$ **(t)** $-4y$ **(u)** $2x + 23$
   (v) $ab + 5bc$ **(w)** $5x + 12y$
5. **(a)** $x^6 + 2x^8 + x^{10}$ **(b)** $4a^4 - 12a^2b^3 + 9b^6$ **(c)** $4p^{10}q^2 - 1$
   (d) $x^4 - y^4$ **(e)** $2a^2 + 32$ **(f)** $a^2 + 2ab + b^2$
   (g) $27a^3 - 9a^2 - 3a + 1$ **(h)** $4a^2 - 36a + 45$ **(i)** $3a^2 + 14a - 1$
   (j) $4x^2 + 28x$ **(k)** $-24y$

6. $p^2z^3(1 + pz - p^2z^2)$ 7. $3x^2(1 + 3xy + 4y^2)$ 8. $3(x^2 + 9)$

9. $2x(x + 4y)(x - 4y)$ 10. $mn^2(4m^2 - 9n)$ 11. $(x + 4y)(x - y)$

12. $(1 - 4p)(1 + 3p)$ 13. $6a^3(3a + 1)(3a - 1)$ 14. $(v - 4)(3u + 2)$

15. $(4r - 3q)(5c - d)$ 16. $20y$ 17. $-63(x + y)(9x + y)$

18. $3(a - 2b)(x - 3)$ 19. $p(n + 7)(n - 4)$ 20. $y(x - 3)(x + 1)$

21. $p(2m - 5n)$ 22. $(x + 2y)(2 - 3x - 6y)$

23. $(4x^2 + y^4z^8)(2x + y^2z^4)(2x - y^2z^4)$ 24. $2(x + 5)(x - 1)$

25. $(6x - 1)(x + 1)$ 26. $(3xy - 1)(2xy - 1)$ 27. $(2 + 3x)(1 - 4x)$

28. $-2(4x - 1)(x - 3)$ 29. $6a(a + 3)^2$ 30. $2x^2y^2(2y - 7x)^2$

31. $(2p - 1)(a + 2)(a - 2)$ 32. $(y + 1)^2(y - 1)$ 33. $3a(a + 10)$

34. $5q(3q - p)$ 35. $(a - 3b)(4x - z)$

36. $(a + 1)(a + 2)(a - 2)$ 37. $3x^3(9x^2 + 1)(3x + 1)(3x - 1)$

38. $(1 - y)(6 + 5y)$ 39. $2a^3b^2c(1 - 4a^2b^2 - 3b^3c)$

40. $(4x^8 + 1)(2x^4 + 1)(2x^4 - 1)$ 41. $a(2a + 3)(4 - a)$

42. $2(2x + 3y)(xy - 1)$ 43. $x^2(3p + q)$

44. $x^2(6x - 1)(4x + 1)$ 45. $(a + b + 7)(a + b - 9)$

46. $(1 + 2b)(a + 4)(a - 4)$ 47. $3(a + 2b)(a + 2b - 3)$ 48. $5(1 + y)(5 - x)$

49. (a) $x = \dfrac{1}{2}$ (b) $y = -6$ (c) $x = \dfrac{1}{15}$ (d) $m = -\dfrac{36}{41}$

(e) $e = -3\dfrac{3}{4}$ (f) $r = -7\dfrac{1}{2}$ (g) $x = 3$ (h) $x = -\dfrac{2}{3}$

(i) $x = 6$ (j) $x = 1\dfrac{1}{4}$ (k) $b = 3\dfrac{3}{4}$ (l) $d = 0$

(m) $m = -2$ (n) $x = \dfrac{5}{8}$ (o) $y = 5$

50. (a) $-2 - 12a - 3a^2$ (b) $\dfrac{6 - 5x}{2(x - 3)}$ (c) $\dfrac{2x - 3}{4}$

51. (a) $13\ 924$ (b) $14\ 396$ (c) 9

52. (a) $x = -\dfrac{4}{3}$ (b) (i) $x = 1$ or 2 (ii) $x = -2$ or 3

53. 18 and 24   54. 18 yrs and 27 yrs   55. 22 yrs

56. 120 km   57. 288   58. 360

59. $1.92   60. 74 km/h   61. 22.5 km, $\dfrac{3}{4}$ h

62. 144 km, 5 min   63. 12 km/h

Test Paper 1

1. (a) 0.043   (b) 4.29×10^{-2}

2. (a) 1.008×10^{-3} (b) 1.5×10^0

3. (a) $\dfrac{1}{5}$ (b) $\dfrac{1}{3}$ (c) -6 (d) $6\dfrac{1}{4}$

4. (a) 2^{35} (b) $\dfrac{1}{4ab^3}$ (c) a^6 (d) $\dfrac{3}{2}\left(\dfrac{a}{b}\right)^7$

5. (a) $2 - 7m + 14m^2 - 12m^3$ (b) $x - 13$

6. **(a)** $4(a^2 + 4)(a + 2)(a - 2)$ **(b)** $(2m - n)(2m - 3n)$

   (c) $3(1 + 2b)(a - 1)$

7. **(a)** 1 **(b)** $\dfrac{1}{n + 1}$

8. **(a)** $x = 4$ **(b)** $x = \dfrac{7}{20}$

Chapter 3

1. **(a)** $x = \dfrac{b + d}{a - c}$ **(b)** $x = 13.2$

2. **(a)** $x = \dfrac{b(a + c)}{ac + bd}$ **(b)** $x = 2$ **3.** **(a)** $x = \dfrac{10abc}{b + 2a}$ **(b)** $x = 20$

4. **(a)** $x = \dfrac{2a - b}{2b - a}$ **(b)** $b = \dfrac{a(x + 2)}{2x + 1}$

5. **(a)** $x = \dfrac{2yk}{2z - y + 1}$ **(b)** $y = x^2z - 1$ **(c)** $k = \dfrac{5bs + 3a}{s + 2}$

   (d) $y = \dfrac{k - 2a}{a - 3}$ **(e)** $a = -\dfrac{7b}{11}$ **(f)** $b = \dfrac{2c}{3ac - 1}$

   (g) $y = \dfrac{5bx - 3}{4b}$ **(h)** $u = \sqrt{\dfrac{mv^2 - 2gpx}{m}}$

6. **(a)** $x = y \pm \sqrt{2y - 5}$ **(b)** $x = \dfrac{y + 5}{3 - z}$ **(c)** $x = a(y - 2)$

   (d) $x = \dfrac{2q - 3p}{3}$ **(e)** $x = \dfrac{a^2 - 7}{a + 3}$ **(f)** $x = \dfrac{8uw}{3(2u - 3w)}$

   (g) $x = -\dfrac{7}{2}y$ **(h)** $x = \sqrt{\dfrac{y^3 + a}{3}}$

7. **(a)** $v = \sqrt{\dfrac{bkp - ak}{b}}$ **(b)** $b = \dfrac{ak}{kp - v^2}$ **8.** **(a)** $\dfrac{5}{8}$ **(b)** $w = \dfrac{Ex}{1 - E}$

9. **(a)** $y = \dfrac{x(x + 1)}{x - 1}$ **(b)** 0 **10.** **(a)** -39 **(b)** $b = \dfrac{6a - y}{3}$

11. **(a)** -6.216×10^{15} **(b)** $y = \dfrac{2(M + 2xz)}{x^2}$

12. **(a)** $g = \dfrac{v^2}{(2h + \sqrt{c^2 + h^2})}$ **(b)** $c = \sqrt{\left(\dfrac{v^2 - 2gh}{g}\right)^2 - h^2}$ **(c)** 61.0

13. **(a)** $c = \dfrac{ab}{3(b - a)}$ **(b)** $9\dfrac{9}{13}$ **14.** **(a)** $r = \sqrt[3]{\dfrac{3v}{4\pi}}$ **(b)** $\dfrac{3}{4}$

15. **(a)** $t = \dfrac{pq(q - 1)}{q^2 - p}$ **(b)** 6 **16.** **(a)** $w = \sqrt{\dfrac{u + v}{6u^2}}$ **(b)** 1.05

17. $a = 60d$; $a = 45$, $b = 15$, $c = 3\dfrac{3}{4}$

18. **(a)** $x = 6$ or -1 **(b)** $y = 0$ or $\dfrac{1}{2}$ **(c)** $y = -1$ or -7

   (d) $t = 7$ or -7 **(e)** $x = 5$ or -5 **(f)** $x = 0$ or -2

   (g) $x = \dfrac{1}{2}$ or -3 **(h)** $x = -\dfrac{1}{4}$ or $\dfrac{7}{5}$ **(i)** $x = 0$ or $\dfrac{2}{5}$

(j) $x = \frac{3}{2}$ or -4 **(k)** $y = \frac{7}{2}$ or -1 **(l)** $x = 5$ or -3

(m) $x = \frac{1}{6}$ or $-\frac{1}{3}$ **(n)** $x = -\frac{8}{3}$ or 1 **(o)** $x = 0$ or 9

(p) $x = -1$ or 6

19. **(a)** $v = \pm 6$ **(b)** $x = \pm\frac{1}{5}$ **(c)** $y = \frac{2}{3}$

(d) $x = -\frac{3}{2}$ or 2 **(e)** $m = \frac{1}{2}$ or $\frac{3}{2}$ **(f)** $x = -\frac{1}{5}$ or $\frac{1}{2}$

(g) $x = -1$ or 2 **(h)** $x = \pm 4$ **(i)** $x = 18$ or -4

(j) $n = -\frac{2}{9}$ or $\frac{1}{3}$ **(k)** $m = -1$ or -2 **(l)** $x = 0$ or -8

(m) $x = \frac{1}{8}$ or 1 **(n)** $x = 10$ or -10

20. **(a)** **(i)** $y = \frac{2}{3}$ **(ii)** $y = 1$ or 10 **(b)** **(i)** $x = 2$ **(ii)** $x = \frac{3}{2}$ or -2

(c) **(i)** $x = 0$ or $\frac{3}{2}$ **(ii)** $x = \frac{5}{2}$ or -1 **(d)** **(i)** $y = \pm 2$ **(ii)** $y = 0$ or 4

(e) **(i)** $x = \pm\frac{7}{3}$ **(ii)** $x = 0$ or $\frac{49}{9}$

(f) **(i)** $x = \pm 1$ **(ii)** $x = -\frac{17}{25}$ or 1 **(iii)** $x = -\frac{8}{25}$ or 1

(g) **(i)** $x = 6$ or -8 **(ii)** $x = 0$ or 3 **(iii)** $x = 1$ or $-\frac{1}{3}$

(h) **(i)** $a = 0$ or $\frac{1}{9}$ **(ii)** $a = \pm\frac{1}{3}$ **(i)** **(i)** $y = \frac{3}{2}$ **(ii)** $y = \frac{3}{4}$ or 3

(j) **(i)** $y = \pm\frac{1}{2}$ **(ii)** $y = \pm\frac{3}{2}$ **(iii)** $y = 1$ or -2

(k) **(i)** $x = -\frac{5}{2}$ **(ii)** $x = \frac{10}{3}$ or -1

(l) **(i)** $x = -\frac{3}{4}$ or $-\frac{1}{2}$ **(ii)** $x = 0$ or $\frac{1}{2}$ or $\frac{5}{6}$

(iii) $x = 0$ or 1 or -2

(m) **(i)** $x = 3$ **(ii)** $x = a, b, c, \ldots, h$

(iii) $x = 0$ or $-\frac{1}{2}$ or $\frac{1}{2}$ or -1

(n) **(i)** $x = 1$ or -2 **(ii)** $x = 2$ or -3

21. **(a)** $a = \dfrac{3A - 9b}{3b}$ **(b)** $a = 6$

22. **(a)** $8\frac{7}{15}$ **(b)** $r = \dfrac{180p}{360 + \pi x}$, $r = 18$ cm

23. $S = 3n$; 138 **(b)** $n = \frac{1}{3}S$; $274, 276$ and 278

24. **(a)** $S = \dfrac{5u + 3v}{8}$ **(b)** $67\frac{1}{2}$ km/h   **(c)** $v = \dfrac{8s - 5u}{3}$; 95 km/h

25. **(a)** $S = \dfrac{270 + 10x}{x}$ **(b)** **(i)** $40   **(ii)** $21.25

     (c) **(i)** 15   **(ii)** 12, $x = \dfrac{270}{s - 10}$

26. **(a)** $(x - 2)$ cm   **(b)** $A = (x - 2)(2x + 3)$

     (c) **(i)** 39 cm^2 **(ii)** $-\dfrac{7}{2}$ or 4   **(d)** 11 cm by 2 cm

27. $x = \dfrac{4}{3}$, 12 cm by $\dfrac{4}{3}$ cm   **28.** $x = 6$, 81 cm^2 **29.** 2 cm

30. 15 cm by 12 cm   **31.** 2 m   **32.** 18

33. 45 yrs, 15 yrs   **34.** 15 yrs, 8 yrs   **35.** 23 km/h

36. **(a)** $(x - 3)(2x + 1)$ **(c)** $1\dfrac{1}{2}$ cm   **37.** 6

38. **(a)** 6 cm^2 **(b)** $3x^2 + 12x - 3$ **(d)** 7 cm

39. ±3, ±4, ±5

40. **(a)** 45 l **(b)** **(i)** $(90 + x)¢$ **(ii)** $\left(\dfrac{3\,150}{90 + x}\right) l$ **(c)** $x = 15$

41. **(a)** $x(2x - 3)$ **(c)** 7 cm and 4 cm

42. **(a)** $\$\left(\dfrac{72}{x}\right)$ **(b)** $\$\left(\dfrac{98}{x + 2}\right)$ **(d)** $x = 12$, $6

43. **(a)** $(x + 4)$ **(b)** $x(x + 4)$
     (d) $x = 7$ or -11 (rejected)   **(i)** $84   **(ii)** $7

Chapter 4

  1. $9.20 per kg   **2.** **(a)** $10\,800   **(b)** **(i)** $832   **(ii)** $24\,000
  3. **(a)** 8\,000   **(b)** 40\,000   **4.** 200 l **5.** 1 day
  6. 12.5%   **7.** 35¢   **8.** 2.5%, 4%
  9. 12%, $1\,073   **10.** $6\,000   **11.** 134.4 g   **12.** 288 boxes
13. 560   **14.** 182 km   **15.** 481 km   **16.** 8.8 m/s
17. $42.50   **18.** 2 h   **19.** $3\,668   **20.** 2 h
21. 438   **22.** $420   **23.** 396   **24.** 8%
25. 30 days   **26.** 313 km   **27.** **(a)** 21 men   **(b)** 12 days
28. **(a)** $5\,000   **(b)** $300, 10%   **29.** **(a)** £4.25   **(b)** 260
30. **(a)** 5 h   **(b)** 84.9%

31. **(a)** 110 km   **(b)** 18.8 min   **(c)** $20\dfrac{5}{6}$ m/s

32. $387.50   **33.** **(a)** $2\,100   **(b)** 35.7%
34. **(a)** 200 cm^3 **(b)** 2\,400 kg/m^3
35. **(a)** $(1, 24), \ldots, (5, 20), (6, 19), \ldots, (12, 13)$; 24 pages
     (b) $(1, 48), \ldots, (19, 30), (20, 29), \ldots, (24, 25)$; 48 pages
36. **(a)** 6   **(b)** 4   **37.** **(c)** 4 cm   **38.** 8 sq. units

39. $\dfrac{1}{4}$

40. **(a)** **(i)** 169×7 **(ii)** 47×9 **(iii)** 64×6
     (b) 2   **(c)** 13×4

41. (a)
$$9\,350$$
$$+\quad 324$$
$$\overline{9\,674}$$

(b)
$$432$$
$$+\quad 432$$
$$\overline{864}$$

(c)
$$734$$
$$+\quad 734$$
$$\overline{1\,468}$$

42. (a) $3 \times 100 - 3 \times 70$　　**(b)** $2 \times 70 - 1 \times 100$　　**43.** $\dfrac{1}{3}$

44. (a)

Time (hours)	Start	1	2	3	4	5	. . .	10
No. of amoeba	1	2	4	8	16	32	. . .	2^{10}

(b)

Time (months)	Start	1	2	3	4	5	. . .	10
No. of breeding pairs	1	1	2	3	5	8	. . .	89

45. (a)

$$\begin{array}{ccccccc}
1 & 5 & 10 & 10 & 5 & 1 \\
1 & 6 & 15 & 20 & 15 & 6 & 1 \\
1 & 7 & 21 & 35 & 35 & 21 & 7 & 1 \\
1 & 8 & 28 & 56 & 70 & 56 & 28 & 8 & 1
\end{array}$$

(b)

$$\dfrac{1}{5} \quad \dfrac{1}{20} \quad \dfrac{1}{30} \quad \dfrac{1}{20} \quad \dfrac{1}{5}$$
$$\dfrac{1}{6} \quad \dfrac{1}{30} \quad \dfrac{1}{60} \quad \dfrac{1}{60} \quad \dfrac{1}{30} \quad \dfrac{1}{6}$$
$$\dfrac{1}{7} \quad \dfrac{1}{42} \quad \dfrac{1}{105} \quad \dfrac{1}{140} \quad \dfrac{1}{105} \quad \dfrac{1}{42} \quad \dfrac{1}{7}$$

46.

No. of plants, N, on the circle	1	2	3	4	5	6	7	. . .	10	50
No. of chords formed	0	1	3	6	10	15	21	. . .	45	1 225

$$N = \frac{N(N-1)}{2}$$

47. Neither
48. (a) 340　　**(b)** 2.75%　　**(c)** 125
49. (a) 30%　　**(b)** \$33.28　　**(c) (i)** \$325　　**(ii)** \$364
50. 336 km
51. (a) 15 km　　**(b)** $1\dfrac{1}{4}$ h

Test Paper 2

1. (a) \$86.40　　**(b) (i)** $n = \dfrac{100}{11}(A - 60)$　　**(ii)** 500

　　(c) $A = 45 + \dfrac{17n}{100}$　　**(d)** 250

2. (a) 20 days　　**(b)** 10 days

3. (a) (i) $\dfrac{50}{x}$ km　　**(ii)** $\dfrac{6}{x - 16}$ km　　**(b)** $\dfrac{50}{x} + \dfrac{6}{x - 16} = 4$

　　(c) $x = 10$ or 20, 2 h 48 min

4. \$1.23 per litre　　**5.** \$28 600

6. (a) \$300　　**(b)** \$208.80　　**(c)** \$413.25　　**(d)** 14.9%

Chapter 5

1. (a) isosceles triangle　　**(b)** $y = 3$　　**(c)** 20 sq. units
　　(d) $(2, 0.6)$ and $(2, 5.4)$

2. (a) $y = 2x + 1$; 27, 101 **(b)** $y = \frac{3}{2}x$; 19.5, 75 **(c)** $y = x^2$; 169, 2 500

3. (c) (i) 3, 4 **(ii)** 3, -1 **(iii)** -2, 4

(iv) $\frac{7}{2}$, 0 **(v)** -1, 0

(d) (i) The lines are parallel.
  (ii) The lines are steeper.
  (iii) The lines have the same y-intercept.
  (iv) The lines pass through the origin.
  (v) The lines slope downwards.

4. (a) Line $a : x = -2$, line $b : y = 3\frac{1}{2}$, line $c : y = -1.5$, line $d : x = 4$,

$A = \left(-2,\ 3\frac{1}{2}\right)$, $B = \left(0,\ 3\frac{1}{2}\right)$, $C = \left(4,\ 3\frac{1}{2}\right)$, $D = (4, 0)$, $E = \left(4,\ -1\frac{1}{2}\right)$,

$F = \left(-2,\ -1\frac{1}{2}\right)$

(c) (i) $y = 0$ **(ii)** $x = 0$

5. (i) line f **(ii)** line b **(iii)** line d
  (iv) line c **(v)** line e **(vi)** line a

6. (a) $x = -2$, $y = 3$ **(b)** $x = 0.7$, $y = 3.4$

7. (b) (i) (3, 7) **(ii)** 15 units **(c)** $x = 3$, $y = 7$

8. $x = 3$, $y = 0$ **9.** No, the two graphs represent parallel lines.

10. $A(4, 4)$, $B(0, 5)$, $C(0, 2)$, $D(1, 0)$ **11.** A, D

12. (a) (4, 7) **(b)** (3, 0) **(c)** (0, 4) **(d)** (2, 5)

13. (a) S$2.20 **(b)** No
  (c) No, he will make a loss of US$3. **(d)** S$30 **(e)** $35

14. (a) 25°C, -6.6°C **(b)** 26.6°F, 98.6°F

15. (a) $y = \frac{8}{3}x$ **(b)** $x = 30$, $y = 0$ **(d) (i)** 61 cm^3 **(ii)** 13 cm

16. (a) $y = \frac{3}{2}x$ **(b)** $x = 20$, $y = 0$ **(d) (i)** 12 cm^3 **(ii)** 9.8 g

17. (b) 32, 110 **(c) (i)** 3.6 cm **(ii)** 22.5 cm^2
  (d) (i) $(32 + 16x)$ cm^2 **(ii)** 5.1 cm

18. (a) (i) $40 **(ii)** $22 **(b) (i)** 200 units **(ii)** 90 units
  (c) (i) 20¢ **(ii)** 10¢

19. (a) S$14 **(b)** £3 **(c)** 115 yen **(d)** £4

20. (a) $550 **(b)** $3 900 **(c)** $350 **(d)** $1 000

21. (a) B **(b)** A **(c)** 08 05, 40 min **(d)** 30 km/h
  (e) 2 times, 10 min **(f)** 20 km/h **(g)** Between 08 00 and 08 10
  (h) 08 15, 20 km from its starting point, 15 min
  (i) 40 km **(j)** 48 km/h **(k)** 08 20, 08 40
  (l) 4 km, 10 km, 17.5 km **(m)** 08 36 **(n)** 34 min

22. (a) Yes, the graph for car X is represented by a straight line.
  (b) Yes, from 09 45 to 10 15, the distance covered remains unchanged.
  (c) $51\frac{1}{5}$ km/h, 27 km/h **(d)** 10 30, 38 km from starting point

(e) 30 km from starting point.   **(f)** 26 km from starting point

(g) 15 min   **(h)** 09 45

23. (a) Car is at rest; 0 km/h   **(b)** 60 km/h   **(c)** 40 km/h

(d) 13 30   **(e)** 50 km from the starting point   **(f)** $53\frac{1}{3}$ km/h

24. (a) 56 km   **(b)** 16 km/h   **(c)** 16 km/h

(d) A straight line from (11 45, 56) to (15 45, 0).   **25.** 11 52

26. Straight line from (12 00, 0) to (14 00, 12); straight line from (12 00, 12), cutting first line where $t = 12\ 30$.

27. $t = 8$ **28. (b)** $37\frac{1}{2}$ km/h   **(c)** 32 km/h

29. (a) $\frac{3}{2}$ **(b)** 45 min   **(c)** $21\frac{1}{3}$ km/h

30. (b) 60 min   **(c)** 15 km/h

(d) 08 40, 10 km from the starting point

31. 17 00, 360 km   **32.** $62\frac{1}{2}$ km/h, 12 42

33. 1 h 11 min, 1 h and 1 h 22 min   **34. (a)** $-4, 6, 0$

(c) (i) 6.1   **(ii)** $-2.2, 2.7$ **(iii)** 0.25   **(vi)** 6.1

35. (a) $a = 1, b = -1$ **(b)** -1.25 **(d)** 1.4 or 3.6

(e) (i) -0.6 **(ii)** 4.5 or 0.5   **(f)** -1.25

(g) 2.5, -1.3 **(i)** $x = 2.5$

36. $b = -3, c = 0$ **37. (a)** (0, 8)   **(b)** $p = 5$

38. (a) $A(-3, 0), B(0, -6), C(2, 0)$ **(b)** $x = -\frac{1}{2}$

39. (a) $P(2, 0), Q(6, 0), R(0, 12)$ **(b)** $d = 5$ **(c)** $k = 4$

40. (b) trapezium   **(c)** $x = 1$ **(d)** 56 sq. units

(e) $(-2.9, 3.9)$

Chapter 6

1. $x = 4, y = -5$ **2.** $x = \frac{1}{2}, y = 1$ **3.** $x = 2, y = -2\frac{1}{2}$

4. $x = 1, y = -1\frac{1}{2}$ **5.** $x = 13, y = 5$ **6.** $x = 4, y = -6$

7. $x = 6, y = 6$ **8.** $x = 3, y = 7$ **9.** $x = -2, y = 4$

10. $x = -\frac{2}{9}, y = \frac{1}{9}$ **11.** $x = -2, y = -\frac{1}{4}$ **12.** $x = 3, y = 6$

13. $x = 7, y = 4$ and $x = \frac{1}{2}, y = \frac{1}{4}$ **14.** $x = -5, y = 6$

15. $x = -1, y = 1$ **16.** $x = 3, y = -4$ **17.** $x = 13, y = 11$

18. $x = 2, y = 3$ **19.** $x = 1, y = \frac{5}{2}$ **20.** $x = 3, y = 4$

21. $x = 1.5, y = 2.4$ **22.** $x = \frac{1}{2}, y = \frac{1}{3}$ **23.** $x = 3, y = 9$

24. $x = 1$, $y = \dfrac{1}{2}$ **25.** $x = 5$, $y = -4$ **26.** $x = \dfrac{1}{3}$, $y = \dfrac{1}{2}$

27. $x = \dfrac{3}{4}$, $y = -\dfrac{1}{9}$ **28.** $x = -1$, $y = -1$ **29.** $x = -2$, $y = 5$

30. $x = -1$, $y = 8$ **31.** $x = 10.5$, $y = -3$

32. **(a)** $x = 9$, $y = -5$ **(b)** $x = \dfrac{1}{6}$, $y = -\dfrac{2}{5}$

33. **(a)** $x = 1$, $y = -1$ **(b)** $x = 7$, $y = -1\dfrac{1}{5}$

34. **(a)** \$4   **(b)** $4x + 3y = 1\,200$; 320
35. A has \$11, B has \$13   **36.** \$5.55   **37.** $\dfrac{13}{27}$
38. 120 paid \$2, 80 paid \$1
39. 10 kg of 80¢/kg biscuits and 15 kg of \$1.20/kg biscuits
40. 12 h, 6 h   **41.** 39   **42.** \$7, \$1
43. **(a)** $AB = 14$ cm, $BC = 8$ cm   **(b)** 44 cm   **(c)** 112 cm^2
44. 36 years old   **45.** 40 cents   **46.** \$3
47. 17 cm, 5 cm   **48.** 40 years old, 8 years old
49. \$32, \$48   **50.** $X = 48$ km/h, $Y = 70$ km/h

51. 5, 15, $\dfrac{1}{3}$ **52.** \$480 000, \$160 000

53. **(a)** 8 cm   **(b)** 30 cm^2
54. 20 cm, 18 cm   **55.** 41 years old, 11 years old
56. 80 km/h   **57.** 9 years old and 33 years old

Test Paper 3

1. **(a)** $\dfrac{1}{2}$, -5 **(b)** $k = -2$ **2.** **(a)** $(1, 1)$ **(b)** $(6, -8)$

3. **(a)** $y = \dfrac{36}{5}x$ **(b)** $x = 15$, $y = 0$ **(d)** **(i)** 2.25 min   **(ii)** 68.5 litres

4. **(a)** 2, -2 **(c)** **(i)** 0.25   **(ii)** 1.8 or 4.2
     (d) -2 **(e)** 3   **(f)** At $(0, 7)$

5. **(a)** $x = -\dfrac{1}{2}$, $y = -16$ **(b)** $x = \dfrac{4}{3}$, $y = -\dfrac{1}{6}$

6. **(a)** 300 km/h   **(b)** 3, 6 minutes   **(c)** 120 km/h
     (d) 12 km   **(e)** 144 km/h   **(f)** 12 04 and 36 seconds

Chapter 7
1. **(a)** $>$ **(b)** $<$ **(c)** $>$ **(d)** $>$ **(e)** $=$
     (f) $>$ **(g)** $>$ **(h)** $<$ **(i)** $<$ **(j)** $<$
2. **(a)** $-1 \leqslant x < 5$ **(b)** $x > -6$ **(c)** $x \leqslant 0$
     (d) $1 \leqslant x \leqslant 4$, x is an integer

3. **(a)** $3 \leqslant a \leqslant 18$ **(b)** $-5 \leqslant b < 7$ **(c)** $x > \dfrac{1}{2}$

     (d) $d \geqslant 2\dfrac{1}{3}$ **(e)** $e \leqslant -3$

5. **(a)** $x = -3, -4$ or -5 **(b)** $x = 7, 8$ or 9 **(c)** $x \leqslant \dfrac{1}{2}$

   (d) $x \leqslant -6$ **(e)** $x > 2$ **(f)** $x > \dfrac{5}{4}$

   (g) $x > 5$ **(h)** $x \geqslant 8$ **(i)** $x \leqslant \dfrac{17}{16}$

   (j) $x \geqslant \dfrac{8}{13}$

6. **(a)** $x < \dfrac{4}{3}$ **(b)** $x \geqslant -\dfrac{6}{5}$ **(c)** $x \leqslant \dfrac{23}{8}$ **(d)** $x < 9$

   (e) $x > 19$ **(f)** $x > \dfrac{1}{4}$ **(g)** $x \geqslant -\dfrac{3}{5}$ **(h)** $x \leqslant \dfrac{15}{52}$

   (i) $x < \dfrac{33}{5}$ **(j)** $x \leqslant \dfrac{103}{21}$

7. **(a)** 7 **(b)** -2 **(c)** $7\dfrac{1}{3}$ **(d)** 5

8. **(a)** $5\dfrac{1}{2}$ **(b)** 6 **9.** 11

10. **(a)** 8 **(b)** 12 **(c)** -14 **(d)** $-\dfrac{7}{2}$

   (e) 4 **(f)** 74

11. **(a)** $x \geqslant 2$ **(b)** $x < 2\dfrac{9}{11}$

Mid-Term Assessment Paper 1

1. **(a)** 81 **(b)** $\dfrac{16}{25}$

2. **(a)** 2.04×10^{-3} **(b)** 1.41×10^{4}

3. $64a^{-6}$ **4.** $\dfrac{3a^3}{2}$ **5.** $x > -\dfrac{1}{2}$

6. **(a)** $3x(4 - 9x)$ **(b)** $(p + 3)(2 - q)$

7. 11.1 **8.** $2\dfrac{3}{5}$ **9.** $\dfrac{1}{a^2}$ **10.** $44

11. $x = \dfrac{3}{4}, y = \dfrac{1}{2}$ **12.** $y = \dfrac{2}{3}$ or $-\dfrac{1}{2}$ **13.** 9 **15.** 9 min

Mid-Term Assessment Paper 2

Section A

1. **(a)** $\dfrac{q^{17}}{p^7}$ **(b)** 9.26×10^{-4} **2.** $\dfrac{4}{2x - 3}$

3. **(a)** $A = \dfrac{xL}{L - x}$ **(b)** -1

4. **(a)** $9m^2 + 3m - 6$ **(b)** $16a$ **5.** 189 km; $10\ 45$

6. **(a)** Town B **(b)** $14\dfrac{2}{7}$ km/h   **(c)** $08\ 30$ and $09\ 45$; $1\dfrac{1}{4}$ h

   (d) 30 km/h

Section B

1. **(a) (i)** 44   **(ii)** 8%   **(b)** 25%   **(c)** $632.50

2. **(a)** $x \geqslant 1$ **(b)** 104 pens

3. **(a)** $(x + 3)$ **(b)** $x(x + 3)$
   (d) $x = 8$ or -11 (rejected), Profit = $16

4. **(a)** $\dfrac{4 - v}{4 + u}$ **(b)** $\dfrac{3}{x(3x - 5)}$ **(c)** $\dfrac{k + 1}{4}$ **(d)** 1

5. **(a)** 0, 4   **(c) (i)** -1.6 and 2.6   **(ii)** -2.25 **(iii)** $x = 0.5$

Chapter 8

1. **(a)** $\triangle ABC \equiv \triangle RST$ (SAS)   **(b)** $\triangle ABE \equiv \triangle BAC$ (SSS)
   (c) $\triangle ABD \equiv \triangle ACD$ (AAS)   **(d)** $\triangle ABE \equiv \triangle CBF$ (AAS)
   (e) $\triangle ABC \equiv \triangle ADC$ (AAS)   **(f)** $\triangle ABC \equiv \triangle DCB$ (SAS)
   (g) $\triangle PQU \equiv \triangle STR$ (RHS)   **(h)** $\triangle ABC \equiv \triangle AED$ (AAS)
   (i) $\triangle PQR \equiv \triangle QPT$ (SAS)   **(j)** $\triangle ADE \equiv \triangle CBF$ (AAS)

2. **(a)** $x = 1.2$ cm, $y = 75°$ **(b)** $x = 1.2$, $y = 4.7$
   (c) $x = 6.5$ cm, $y = 8.6$ cm   **(d)** $x = 4.8$, $y = 42°$
   (e) $x = 1.5$, $y = 5$ **(f)** $x = 56°$, $y = 18$

3. **(a)** $\triangle XYZ \equiv \triangle DEB$ (SAS)   **(b)** 6 cm^2

4. **(a)** $\triangle PQR \equiv \triangle PST$ (AAS)   **(b)** $RS = 41.5$ **(c)** 60°

5. $\triangle LMY \equiv \triangle NLX$ (AAS)   **6.** $\triangle ACQ \equiv \triangle ABR$ (RHS)

7. **(a)** $\triangle GDC$ (AAS)   **(b) (i)** 53°   **(ii)** 4 cm   **(iii)** 6 cm^2

8. $e = 6$, $f = 15$ **9.** $x = 12$, $y = 3$ **10.** $b = 15\frac{5}{7}$, $c = 12\frac{4}{7}$

11. $v = 18$, $u = 9$ **12.** $h = 10$, $k = 15$ **13.** $u = 4.4$, $v = 6\frac{2}{3}$

14. $s = 15$, $t = 12$ **15.** $p = 20$, $q = 16$

16. $e = 8$, $f = 6\frac{1}{4}$, $g = 15$, $h = 9$ **17.** $p = 10$, $q = 2\frac{2}{3}$, $r = 6\frac{3}{4}$

18. $a = 7\frac{1}{2}$, $b = 1.92$ **19.** $x = 3$, $y = 7\frac{1}{2}$

20. $m = 12\frac{1}{2}$, $n = 3$ **21.** $f = 3\frac{1}{3}$, $g = 24$

22. **(a)** $\triangle AED$ **(b)** $\triangle AE$, AC **(c)** 6, 6

23. **(a) (i)** $\triangle XZC$ **(ii)** $5\frac{1}{3}$ cm   **(b) (i)** $\triangle WAB$ **(ii)** $1\frac{1}{11}$ cm

24. **(a)** $\triangle ABC$, $\triangle GDC$, $\triangle FEC$ **(b)** $AB = 3$ cm, $DE = 12.5$ cm, $EF = 9$ cm
   (c) $PQ = 4$ cm, $Q\hat{P}R = 36.9°$

25. **(a)** 8 cm   **(b)** 6 cm

26. 3 cm, 3.9 cm, 5 cm, 6.4 cm and 4.1 cm; 24 cm

27. $6\frac{2}{3}$ m   **28.** 48 m   **29.** 10.8 m

30. **(a)** 12 km   **(b)** 18 km   **(c)** 20.4 km

Chapter 9

1. **(a)** 19.8 cm   **(b)** 69.3 cm^2 **2.** **(a)** 150°   **(b)** 42 cm

3. 246.4 cm^2, 35.2 cm, 119.2 cm

4. **(a)** 1 155 cm^2 **(b)** 184 cm   **(c)** $\frac{13}{18}$

5. **(a)** $50(\pi - 2)$ cm^2 **(b)** $13\frac{2}{3}\pi$ cm^2 **(c)** 60π cm^2 **6.** 1 : 1

7. **(a)** 70°   **(b)** 11 cm   **(c)** 6.3 cm   **(d)** 49.8 cm

8. **(a)** 15.20 cm^2 **(b)** 7.8 cm^2 **(c)** 1.27 cm^2 **(d)** 20 cm^2

9. **(a)** 18°   **(b)** 78.5 cm^2 **10.** 30   **11.** $222\frac{3}{4}$ cm^2

12. **(a)** $\triangle STR$ **(b)** $3\frac{3}{5}$ cm   **(c)** $\frac{81}{25}$

13. **(a)** $\triangle PQR$ and $\triangle TSR$ **(b)** $\frac{1}{5}$ **(c)** 65   **(d)** 750 cm^2

14. **(a)** $\triangle ABF \equiv \triangle DEF$ (AAS)   **(b)** $\triangle ACD$ **(c)** **(i)** 1 : 1   **(ii)** 1 : 2
(d) 4 cm   **(e)** 48 cm^2 **(f)** 48 cm^2

15. **(a)** 30 cm^2 **(b)** 7.5 cm   **(c)** 2.5 cm^2

16. **(a)** $\triangle AEF \equiv \triangle DEB$ (AAS)   **(b)** **(i)** 5.4 cm   **(ii)** 15 cm   **(iii)** $43\frac{3}{4}$ cm^2

(c) $43\frac{3}{4}$ cm^2

17. 1 080 kg   **18.** **(a)** 16 cm^3 **(b)** $2\frac{1}{3}$ cm^2

19. **(a)** 24 cm   **(b)** 7 cm   **(c)** 1 : 9

20. **(a)** 1 : 5   **(b)** 500 g   **(c)** 275 cm^2 **(d)** $20\frac{5}{6}$ g/cm^3

21. **(a)** 3 : 4   **(b)** 256 g   **(c)** 120 cm^3, $284\frac{4}{9}$ cm^3

22. **(a)** 60 cm   **(b)** 5 000 cm^2 **(c)** 64 : 125

23. **(a)** 3 : 2   **(b)** 27 : 8   **(c)** 27 : 8

24. 15 cm, 367.2 cm^2, 6.48 g   **25.** 9 cm   **26.** 20 cm

27. **(a)** 4 : 5   **(b)** 1 100.8 cm^3

28. **(i)** 3 : 2   **(ii)** 6 cm   **(iii)** 4 cm, 6 cm, 4 cm

29. **(a)** 25 : 4   **(b)** 25 cm^3

30. **(a)** 35 cm   **(b)** 4 : 25   **(c)** 16 cm^3

31. **(a)** $l = 34$ cm, $S = 0.63$ m^2, $V = 0.16$ m^3

(b) $l = 6$ cm, $S = 6\frac{1}{4}$ cm^2, $V = 4.687\ 5$ cm^3

32. **(a)** 4 : 3   **(b)** 16 : 9   **(c)** 64 : 27

33. 10.27 cm, 34.02 cm^2 **34.** 33.02 tonnes   **35.** 175 cm^2

36. 64 : 27   **37.** **(a)** 115.5 cm^3 **(b)** 34.2 cm^3 **(c)** 1 136.2 g

38. (a) $150\frac{6}{7}$ cm^3 (b) $\frac{3}{4}$ cm   (c) 38.3%

39. (a) (i) 1 232 cm^3 (ii) 6.16 kg   (b) (i) 1 150.81 cm^3 (ii) 6.59%
40. (a) 586 cm^2 (b) 351.6 cm^3 (c) \$175.80
41. (a) 4.5 cm   (b) (i) 178·32 l (c) 8.22 cm
42. (a) 792 cm^3 (b) 72 cm^2 43. 93π cm^3, 75π cm^2

44. (a) $\frac{4}{3}\pi$ cm^3 (b) $\frac{22}{7}$ cm   45. 42π cm^2

46. (a) 146 cm^2 (b) 3 718.67 cm^3 (c) 74.37 kg
47. (a) (i) 2 112 cm^3 (ii) 264   (iii) 70

    (b) 1 344 cm^3 (c) 0.893 g/cm^3

48. (a) 11.1 min   (b) (i) 28 cm   (ii) 20.2 cm   (c) 4 cm
49. 1.117 kg, 14 132 kg/m^3 50. 1.512 cm

51. (a) 8.59 cm   (b) 405 cm^2 52. 757.5 cm^2 53. $99\frac{3}{7}$ cm^2

54. 270 cm^3 55. 15 cm   56. 108π cm^2 57. 702 cm^3
58. (a) 4 cm   (b) 245.08 cm^3 59. (a) 2.52 cm   (b) 12.4 cm

60. (a) (i) $4\frac{1}{2}$ m   (ii) 148.5 m^3 (b) 31 min 11 s

61. (a) 3 : 4   (b) 9 : 16   (c) (i) 1 920 cm^3 (ii) 729 g

Test Paper 4

1. (a) $E\hat{G}F = C\hat{B}D$, $E\hat{F}G = B\hat{C}D$, $EG = BD$, $\triangle BCD \equiv \triangle GFE$ (AAS)
   (b) 15 cm   (c) 2 : 3   (d) 14.7 cm^2

2. (a) $51\frac{1}{3}$ cm^2 (b) $18\frac{2}{3}$ cm^2, $34\frac{2}{3}$ cm

3. (a) 3 cm   (b) (i) 15π cm^2 (ii) 135π cm^2 (iii) 210π cm^2
4. (a) 5 : 4   (b) 8 m^2 (c) 12.5 kg   (d) 500 cm^3
5. (a) 462 cm^3 (b) 154 cm^3 (c) 3.32 cm

Chapter 10

1. (a) $c = \sqrt{a^2 - b^2}$ (b) $c = a \sin x$ (c) $c = a \cos y$

   (d) $c = b \tan x$ (e) $c = \dfrac{b}{\tan y}$

2. (a) $\frac{1}{5}$ (b) $\frac{9}{25}$ (c) $-\frac{7}{12}$ (d) 1

3. (a) $\frac{4}{3}x$ (b) 36.9°   4. $4\sqrt{3}$, $12 - 12\sqrt{3}$

5. (a) $25\sqrt{3}$ cm^2 (b) $\frac{1}{2}$ (c) $\frac{1}{2}$

6. (a) $(2x + 2)^2 + (x - 4)^2 = (2x + 3)^2$ (b) 56 cm   (c) 16.3°

7. (a) 204 cm², 66 cm (b) 53.1°, 53.1°
   (c) trapezium; $A\hat{B}D = B\hat{D}C = 53.1°$, ∴ $AB \parallel CD$.
8. $AE = 4$ cm 9. (a) 4.34 cm (b) 23.6° (c) 7.72 cm
10. (a) 4 cm (b) 6 cm (c) $4\sqrt{3}$ cm (d) $2\sqrt{3}$ cm
11. (a) 10.5 cm (b) 10.4 cm (c) 2.68 cm 12. 7.04 cm
13. (a) 9 cm (b) $56\frac{1}{4}\pi$ cm (c) 7.5 cm (d) 4.97 cm (e) 112.9°
14. 10 cm 15. 10 cm 16. 9.22 cm, 5.86 cm 17. 60 cm²
18. (a) $x = 71.8°$, $y = 3.79$ (b) $x = 27.4°$, $y = 4.77$, $z = 17.2°$
19. (a) 21.7 cm (b) 37.5 cm (c) 50 cm 20. 35.6 m
21. 33.7 m 22. 5.64 m, 6.39 m
23. (a) 50° (b) 2.1 m 24. 1.53 cm 25. 13.2 m
26. 3.10 m 27. 11.7 m 28. 22.7 m
29. (a) 1.5 cm (b) 73.7° 30. 83.6°, 71.6 cm²
31. (a) 120 m (b) 57.6° 32. (a) 11.3 m (b) 110 m 33. 1.61 m
34. (a) 5 cm (b) $\frac{10}{13}$ (c) 45° (d) 22.4°
35. (a) 18 cm (b) 73.7°
36. (a) (i) 20 (ii) 18 (b) (i) $\frac{5}{13}$ (ii) $-\frac{12}{13}$ (iii) $-\frac{12}{5}$
37. (a) 3 cm² (b) (i) $\frac{4}{5}$ (ii) $-\frac{3}{2}$ (iii) $\frac{3}{5}$
38. (a) 1.24 cm (b) 45° (c) $\frac{9}{4}(\pi - 2)$ cm²

Chapter 11

6. (a) (i) $A_1(-1, 1)$, $B_1(0, 1)$, $C_1(1, 3)$, $D_1(-2, 3)$
      (ii) $A_2(3, 3)$, $B_2(2, 3)$, $C_2(1, 1)$, $D_2(4, 1)$
      (iii) $A_3(-3, -1)$, $B_3(-3, 0)$, $C_3(-5, 1)$, $D_3(-5, -2)$
   (b) (i) $A_1(-1, 0)$, $B_1(-3, 1)$, $C_1(-2, -1)$, $D_1(-3, -2)$
      (ii) $A_2(2, 6)$, $B_2(0, 7)$, $C_2(1, 5)$, $D_2(0, 4)$
   (c) (i) $A_1\left(1, 1\frac{1}{3}\right)$, $B_1(1, 2)$, $C_1(2, 2)$
      (ii) $A_2\left(7\frac{1}{2}, 10\right)$, $B_2\left(7\frac{1}{2}, 15\right)$, $C_2(15, 15)$

8. (b) (i) $\triangle B : (3, 4), (1, 3), (2, 2)$ (ii) $\triangle C : (5, 2), (4, 4), (3, 3)$
      (iii) $\triangle D : (0, -1), (2, 0), (1, 1)$ (iv) $\triangle E : (1, -1), (2, -3), (3, -2)$
      (v) $\triangle F : (-1, 4), (-2, 2), (-3, 3)$ (vi) $\triangle G : (-3, 6), (-2, 4), (-1, 5)$
      (vii) $H : \left(\frac{1}{2}, 2\right), (1, 1), \left(1\frac{1}{2}, 1\frac{1}{2}\right)$

9. (a) Translation -5 units in the x-direction and 1 unit in the y-direction.
   (b) 90° clockwise rotation about the origin.
   (c) Reflection about the line $x = 5$.
   (d) Reflection about the y-axis.

10. (a) (4, 8)   (b) (2, 4)   (c) (0, 0)

11. (a) (i) (2, 3)   (ii) $(-2, -3)$ (iii) $(0, -3)$ (iv) (2, 0)   (v) $(3, -7)$

     (b) (i) $(0, -6)$ (ii) (0, 6)   (iii) $(-2, 6)$ (iv) (0, 9)   (v) (1, 2)

     (c) (i) $(-5, 0)$ (ii) (5, 0)   (iii) $(-7, 0)$ (iv) $(-5, 3)$ (v) $(-4, -4)$

12. (a) $X(-2, -1)$, $Y(-4, -1)$, $Z(-2, -4)$, $A(2, -1)$, $B(4, -1)$, $C(2, -4)$

     (b) Reflection about the x-axis.

13. (b) (i) $A_1(-1, 1)$, $B_1(-2, 2)$, $C_1(-3, 0)$, $A_2(-2, 2)$, $B_2(-3, 3)$, $C_2(-4, 1)$

       (ii) 90° anticlockwise rotation about $(-1, 0)$.

     (c) (ii) Reflection in the line $y = x$.

       (iii) Reflection about the x-axis.

14. (a) $A_1\left(5, 2\frac{1}{2}\right)$, $B_1\left(12\frac{1}{2}, 2\frac{1}{2}\right)$ (b) $X(4, -1)$, $Y(4, -4)$

15. (b) 180° rotation about the origin.

16. P is a translation of -1 unit in the x-direction and -3 units in the y-direction. Q is an enlargement with centre $(-2, -2)$ and scale factor 2. R is an enlargement with centre $(0, 4)$ and scale factor 2.

17. (a) Translation 4 units in the x-direction.

     (b) Reflection in the y-axis.

     (c) 180° rotation about $(0, 0)$.

     (d) 90° anticlockwise rotation about $(0, 2)$.

18. (a) P – 90° clockwise rotation about the origin.

        Q – reflection about the y-axis.

     (b) Reflection in the line $y = -x$.

19. (a) (i) (7, 0)   (ii) 180°   (b) (i) $(-2, 0)$ (ii) 2

     (c) $(4, -3)$, $(7, -3)$, $(6, -1)$

20. (a) (i) P is a 180° rotation about $\left(6\frac{1}{2}, 2\right)$. Q is a translation 6 units in the x-direction and 3 units in the y-direction.

       (ii) 180° rotation about $\left(9\frac{1}{2}, 3\frac{1}{2}\right)$.

     (b) Enlargement about $(3, -2)$ with scale factor $\frac{3}{2}$.

Test Paper 5

1. 484.9 m

2. (a) 0.678   (b) 16.8°   (c) 0.470   (d) 20.8°

3. (a) 58.2°   (b) 5.43   (c) 10.2

4. (a) $x = 2$

     (b) Transformation X is a 90° clockwise rotation about $\left(2\frac{1}{2}, 1\frac{1}{2}\right)$.

     (e) (i) Translation -3 units in the x-direction.

       (ii) Reflection about the line $x = \frac{1}{2}$.

5. (a) Transformation P is a reflection in the y-axis. Transformation Q is a translation 6 units in the x-direction. Transformation R is a reflection in the x-axis.

     (b) (i) The single transformation is a reflection in the line $x = 3$.

       (ii) The single transformation is a 180° rotation about the origin.

Chapter 12

1. **(a)** 6   2. **(a)** 30°   **(b)** 8 h   **(c)** $8\frac{1}{3}\%$ **(d)** 4 : 7

3. **(a)** 100   **(b)** 12%   **(c)** A
   (e) Either the quiz is very easy or this group of Sec 2 students are good in Science.

4. **(a)** bar chart   **(b)** 5   **(c)** 20   **(d)** 12   **(e)** 36
   (f) 25   **(g)** 1.44

5. **(b)** **(i)** 30   **(ii)** 50%   **(iii)** 120

6. **(a)** 54°   **(b)** 81°   **(c)** 75°   **(d)** 1 848   7. 9

8. **(b)** **(i)** pie chart **(ii)** bar chart   **(c)** 15%   **(d)** 120°

9. **(a)** 18   **(b)** 30%   **(c)** 2 500 g or 2.5 kg

10. **(a)** 130 coins   **(b)** $40.50   **(c)** 9   **(d)** 11.5%
    (e) 35.8%   **(f)** 83.1°

12. **(a)** $30 000   **(b)** $135 000   **(c)** Household items

    (d) $\frac{10}{31}$ **(e)** $\frac{23}{80}$ **(f)** $\frac{4}{9}$ **(g)** $50 000

    (h) 50%

13. English : 54°, 6; 2nd Language : 36°, 4; Humanities : 72°, 8; Mathematics : 54°, 6; Science : 54°, 6; Art and Craft : 27°, 3; Moral Education : 27°, 3; Physical Education : 36°, 4

14. **(a)** 152 500   **(b)** February   **(c)** $13\frac{1}{3}\%$

Chapter 13

1. **(a)** 4   **(b)** 7   **(c)** 6
2. **(a)** 4.2   **(b)** 2   **(c)** 17.24°
3. **(a)** **(i)** 1   **(ii)** 2   **(b)** 6
4. **(b)** 3   **(c)** 100   **(d)** 2.6   **(e)** 60%
5. **(a)** 12   **(c)** 1, 3   **(d)** 3.2
6. **(a)** 3   **(b)** 4   **(c)** 3.75

7. **(b)** $\frac{3}{5}$ **(c)** $2 \leqslant x < 3, 2 \leqslant x < 3$ 8. **(c)** 8, 24   **(d)** 3

9. **(b)** 5.25   **(c)** 7   **(d)** 6   **(e)** 9
10. **(b)** 26   **(c)** 6   **(d)** 2   **(e)** 26.9%
11. **(a)** 240   **(b)** 24   **(c)** 4th day, 35   **(d)** 4th and 8th day
12. **(b)** 6.4, 7, 7   13. **(c)** 2, 2, 2.58   14. 442 g
15. **(a)** 195   **(b)** 19   16. 13
17. **(a)** 18.3, 12, 18   **(b)** 8   18. 15.5

Test Paper 6

1. **(a)** 60   **(b)** 40%   **(c)** 216°

2. **(b)** **(i)** 12   **(ii)** 5   **(iii)** $\frac{8}{25}$

   (c) 70   **(d)** 2.8, 2, 3

3. (a) 128°   (b) (i) 1 582   (ii) 452   (iii) 8 : 7
4. (a) (i) 182   (ii) 35.2%   (b) school bus
5. (a) 5   (b) 4, 4

Chapter 14

1. (a) $x^3 + 5x^2 + 4x + 15$ (b) $4x^4 + 8x^2 + 3x - 14$
2. (a) $x^3 - 6x^2 - 7x + 10$
   (b) $2a^6 - 5a^5 - 10a^4 + 11a^3 - 12a^2 + 3a - 8$
3. $10p^2 + 7pq + 4q^2$ 4. $9a^2 - 10ab + b^2$ 5. $-10a^3 + 2a^2 + 4a - 1$
6. $a^4 - a^3 + 3a^2 + 2a - 6$ 7. $7x^3 - x^2 - 4x + 16$ 8. $-3a^2 + 7ab$
9. $11x^3 + 7x^2 - 3x + 4$ 10. $4x^5 + 6x^4 - 8x^3 + 3x^2 + 2x - 1$
11. $13x^4 - 27x^2 + 5$ 12. $3x^2 - 2x - 4$ 13. $x^2 + 2x - 1$
14. $4x^3 + 5x^2 - 5x + 2$ 15. $2x^4 - 3x^3 + x^2 + 1$ 17. (a) $x - 2$ (b) $x + 2$
18. (a) $11x^5 + x^4 - 10x^3 - 6x^2 - 30x - 15$ (b) $2x^4 + 108x^3 + 4x^2 - 60x - 22$
    (c) x^4 (d) 0
19. (a) $3x\left(6x^2 + \frac{4}{3}x - 4\right)$ (b) $(x + 1)(3x^3 - 3x^2 + 2x + 6) - 10$
    (c) $(x^2 - x + 2)(4x^2 - x - 8) - 6x + 14$
    (d) $(x^3 - x^2 + x - 1)(x + 3) - 4x + 7$
    (e) $(2x - 1)\left(2x^2 + x - \frac{3}{2}\right) + \frac{3}{2}$ (f) $(x - 3)(3x^2 + 9x + 27) + 74$
    (g) $(2x^2 + 2x - 1)\left(4x^2 - 4x + \frac{11}{2}\right) - 15x + \frac{21}{2}$
20. (a) $a = 3, b = 2, c = -1$ (b) $a = 2, b = -3$
    (c) $a = 1, b = -1, c = 4$ (d) $a = 3, b = -2$
    (e) $p = 3, q = -1, r = -7$ (f) $A = 2, B = 4$
    (g) $a = -2, b = 3, c = 1$ (h) $a = -2, b = -4, c = 2$
21. (a) $x = \frac{y + 1}{3}$ (b) $z = \frac{5 - 4y}{2}$ (c) $x = \frac{9 - 2z}{12}$ (d) $z = \frac{9 - 12x}{2}$
22. (a) $x = \frac{z - 1}{2}$ (b) $y = \frac{2z + 1}{12}$
23. (a) $x = -\frac{14}{3}z - 59$ (b) $z = \frac{3}{2}(y - 9)$
24. (a) $y = \frac{3}{4}(x - 1)$ (b) $x = \frac{2z + 1}{3}$ (c) $y = \frac{z - 1}{2}$
25. (a) $x = \frac{1 - 3z}{7}$ (b) $y = z$ 26. $w = 1 - x$
27. $x = 10 - 4w$
28. (a) $7 - 14x$ (b) $33m^5 - 21m^4 - 8m^3 + 3m^2 - m - 1$
29. $a^4 - 3a^3 - 6a^2 + 5a - 4$
30. (a) quotient $= 2x^3 - x^2 + x - 3$, remainder $= 3$
    (b) quotient $= x^2 + 3x - 6$, remainder $= 22x - 19$
31. (a) $-9, 0$ (b) $-4, 3, -2$
32. (a) (i) $x = 3(4 - y)$ (ii) $x = 10 - 7z$ (b) $x = 7.2, y = 1.6$

Final Term Assessment Paper 1

1. $a = 1, b = -2$
2. $7, 7$
3. $x = 31°, y = 1.5$ cm
4. $(3x - 8)(x + 6)$
5. $\dfrac{7x - 13}{2(x - 3)(3x - 1)}$
6. $x = 12, y = 3$
7. **(a)** 36 km/h **(b)** 400 m
8. $x = \dfrac{4}{3}$
9. 11.6 cm
10. **(a)** 1 cm **(b)** $\dfrac{4}{5}$ **(c)** 4
11. $k = -2$
12. $\dfrac{4\pi}{3}$
13. **(a)** 1 000 stamps **(b)** 108° **(c)** $\dfrac{11}{30}$
14. **(a)** 2 : 3 **(b)** 54 g

Final Term Assessment Paper 2

Section A

1. $1 + x - x^3 + x^4$
2. **(a)** $x = \dfrac{15y + 5}{3}$ **(b)** $x = \dfrac{8 - 15z}{3}$
3. $x^2 + x - 3; -8$
4. 432 cm^2
5. **(a)** Reflection in the y-axis.
   (b) Enlargement with centre X and scale factor 3.
   (c) Translation 20 units in the x-direction and -30 units in the y-direction.
6. **(a)** 80 **(b)** 70% **(c)** 3.925

Section B

1. 1.6 m
2. **(a)** $\triangle AXY \equiv \triangle XBZ$ (AAS) **(b)** $\triangle AXY$ and $\triangle ABC$
   (c) **(i)** 1 : 1 **(ii)** 1 : 2 **(iii)** 1 : 4 **(d)** 8.4 cm^2
3. **(a)** 30° **(b)** 3.46 cm **(c)** 7.65 cm^2
4. **(a)** $x = 9$ **(b)** 2 **(c)** 54.4% **(d)** 90°
5. **(b)** 2; (2, 0.5) **(c)** **(ii)** 90° anticlockwise rotation about (2, 2.5).